Making Gluten-Free Living Easy!

Cecelia's Marketplace

Kalamazoo, Michigan

www.CeceliasMarketplace.com

Gluten/Casein/Soy Free

GROCERY SHOPPING GUIDE

2010 EDITION

Dr. Mara Matison
Dainis Matison

khP

Kal-Haven Publishing

Cecelia's Marketplace
Gluten/Casein/Soy Free Grocery Shopping Guide

by Dr. Mara Matison & Dainis Matison

Kal-Haven Publishing
P.O. Box 20383
Kalamazoo, MI 49019 U.S.A.

ISBN 978-0-9794094-6-2

2010 Edition

Printed in the United States of America
Cover illustration: Lilita Austrins

CONTENTS

About the Authors

The co-author of this book, Dr. Mara Matison, received her Doctor of Dental Surgery degree from University of Detroit Mercy, and her Bachelor of Arts degree in Psychology from Villanova University. Her husband and co-author, Dainis Matison, received his Master of Science degree in Information Technology and Bachelor of Arts degree in Finance from Ball State University. They are both members of Celiac Disease Foundation, Celiac Sprue Association, Gluten Intolerance Group, and Talk About Curing Autism. These are nationwide organizations that support people with celiac disease, gluten intolerance, gluten sensitivitiy and autism.

Cecelia's Marketplace was established by both Mara and Dainis in 2006, soon after Mara was diagnosed with celiac disease. The couple struggled with Mara's huge lifestyle change, which included adhering to a strict gluten-free diet. Shopping trips to the grocery store were very frustrating. Spending time calling food manufacturers to find out if products were gluten-free seemed like a daily routine. They knew there had to be an easier way, so they decided to compile a gluten-free grocery shopping guide. Since then, Mara has also been diagnosed with a casein and soy intolerance, which brought about the need for the *Gluten/Casein Free Grocery Shopping Guide* and the *Gluten/Casein/Soy Free Grocery Shopping Guide*.

Thanks to all three of Cecelia's Marketplace Grocery Shopping Guides, grocery shopping now has become easier for not only the authors, but also their families, friends and thousands of grocery shoppers nationwide.

Preface - Note to the Reader

Cecelia's Marketplace Gluten/Casein/Soy Free Grocery Shopping Guide has been written to help people that are in search of gluten-free, casein-free and soy-free (GFCFSF) products. Whether you are on a GFCFSF diet, prepare GFCFSF meals for yourself or others, or just enjoy eating GFCFSF foods, this book is for you. It will help guide you to easy grocery shopping and eliminate the frustration and headaches that you've experienced trying to find GFCFSF products. This guide is also great for restaurant owners, chefs, dieticians, family members, husbands, wives, friends, and others who shop for, or prepare GFCFSF foods. For those that are not familiar with GFCFSF cooking or GFCFSF dining out, we have included three sections in the front of the book: *What is Gluten, Casein & Soy, Clean Kitchen Tips, and Gluten/Casein/Soy Free Dining Out*.

We have alphabetized our *Gluten/Casein/Soy Free Grocery Shopping Guide* to help you quickly find brand names of the GFCFSF products. The guide is easy to use: just pick a product, look it up, and you'll have GFCFSF brands at your fingertips. This book is small enough so that it can be carried with you to the grocery store when searching for products. Use it anytime, anywhere. In addition to the grocery shopping guide, there is a section in the back of the book that lists GFCFSF over the counter (OTC) medications. GFCFSF shopping has never been easier. Treasure this book and enjoy all the GFCFSF foods that are available!

Due to periodic changes in ingredients and new products, *Cecelia's Marketplace Gluten/Casein/Soy Free Grocery Shopping Guide* will be updated annually. Look for the new edition every year.

A percentage of our proceeds are donated to nationwide nonprofit organizations that support people with celiac disease, gluten intolerance, autism, and other food sensitivities.

Dr. Mara Matison
Dainis Matison

Acknowledgments

There are many people that have contributed to the creation of this book. The support from our family and friends has made this journey more enjoyable. Lauma for data research and editing, Lilita A. for editing, cover illustration, and all the gluten-free meals that kept us going; Mik for editing, critiquing and successful business strategies; Ray for all the reference materials and guidance to becoming successful entrepreneurs; Ligita supporting us and all the delicious gluten-free recipes along the way; Lija, Liana, Annette, & Leah for data collection; Lilita M. for showing us 'The Secret'; Velta and Ilga for believing in us; Jonnie Bryant for all the publishing advice and knowledge; Dr. Heidi Gjersoe for the diagnosis and support; Larisa Kins for book page layout & cover design; Jeff Matson at Creative Group for logo design; Natural Health Center for the wonderful gluten-free book signing events; Dr. Arnis Pone, Dr. Jason Ham, Kal-Haven Publishing, McNaughton & Gunn, and all our fellow "celiacs" for all the support.

Warning - Disclaimer

What is Gluten, Casein & Soy?

Gluten is a special type of protein that is most commonly found in wheat, rye, and barley. It is comprised of two main protein groups: gliadins, and gluteins. People who have celiac disease, gluten intolerance, or gluten sensitivity may suffer from chronic digestive problems when ingesting foods that contain gluten. Gluten is found in most cereals, breads, pastas, soups, and pizza crusts. It may also be hidden in foods such as seasonings, salad dressings, sauces, additives and natural flavors.

Casein is a protein found in milk. It is a phosphoprotein, which is a collection of proteins bound to phosphoric acid. Casein is found in products containing milk, such as cheese, butter, cream, yogurt, ice cream and any other derivative of milk. Many people suffering from celiac disease or gluten/casein intolerance cannot properly digest this protein.

Soy is derived from the soybean, also called the soya bean. Common forms of soy include soy meal, soy flour, soy milk, soy sauce, tofu, textured vegetable protein, tempeh, soy lecithin and soybean oil. Various studies show that most soy allergic individuals may safely eat products that contain soy lecithin and soybean oil, since they do not contain the soy protein. On the contrary, other studies show that any form of soy should be avoided for those individuals with either a soy intolerance or soy allergy.

Maintaining a strict gluten/casein/soy free diet has shown to greatly improve the symptoms of celiac disease, and gluten/casein/soy intolerance. After gluten, casein and soy are eliminated from the diet, the digestive tract begins to heal and the symptoms normally start to disappear after a few weeks[1].

[1] www.mayoclinic.com/health/celiac-disease/DS00319/DSECTION=treatments-and-drugs

Clean Kitchen Tips

It is very important prior to preparing a gluten-free, casein-free, and soy-free (GFCFSF) meal, to clean the surrounding area including, pots, pans, utensils and any other items being used. Bread crumbs, flour particles or other gluten, casein or soy containing foods left in the cooking area can potentially contaminate a GFCFSF meal.

Here are some tips to help prevent gluten, casein and soy contamination:

- Use an uncontaminated sponge to wash all working surfaces with soap and water.
- Clean and inspect pots, pans, utensils, cutting boards and other kitchenware for gluten, casein and soy residue.
- Use clean kitchen hand towels.
- If grilling, place aluminum foil over the grilling area.
- Use squeeze bottle mustard, ketchup, peanut butter, jelly/jam, or other condiments to prevent cross-contamination.
- Avoid using wooden utensils. Gluten, casein and soy residue can stay embedded in wooden utensils and cutting boards.
- Use a separate toaster for GFCFSF bread, rice cakes, etc..
- In commercial kitchens, if using latex/rubber gloves, make sure the gloves are not coated with powder (starch).
- Do not deep fry foods in contaminated oil (e.g. from breaded chicken wings, breaded chicken tenders, mozzarella sticks).

Gluten/Casein/Soy Free Dining Out

Nationwide restaurant chains offering *gluten-free menus:

Austin Grill
Biaggi's Ristorante
Bonefish Grill
Bugaboo Creek Steakhouse
Carino's Italian Grill
Carraba's Italian Grill
Charlie Brown's Steakhouse
Cheeseburger In Paradise
Chili's Grill & Bar
Claim Jumper Restaurants
Fleming's Prime Steakhouse & Wine Bar
Legal Sea Foods
Romano's Macaroni Grill
Ninety Nine Restaurant
Old Spaghetti Factory
On The Border Mexican Grill
Outback Steakhouse
P.F. Chang's China Bistro
Pasta Pomadoro
Pei Wei Asian Diner
Pizza Fusion
Uno Chicago Grill
Weber Grill Restaurant
Wildfire Restaurants
Z. Tejas Southwestern Grill

*These menus are only gluten-free. Please explain to the wait staff that the meal needs to be gluten-free, casein-free and soy-free.

Other Products Available
by Cecelia's Marketplace

Grocery Shopping Guides:
Gluten-Free
Gluten/Casein Free

Other Products:
GF Dining Out Cards
Gluten-Free Safety Labels

FREE Email Sign-Up:
Gluten-Free Product of the Day

For **Product Alerts** or more information about our products please visit us online:

www.CeceliasMarketplace.com

Our Data Collection

The product information in this book was collected between May 2009 - December 2009. The information was received from product manufacturers and major supermarkets via internet, e-mail, phone, mail or product labels.

The Food and Drug Administration (FDA) has proposed to define the term "gluten-free" as containing less than 20 parts per million (ppm) gluten. This regulation was scheduled to be issued in 2008. Some food manufacturers have already begun testing their products for the presence of gluten. Those products that have not passed this test have been excluded from this book. Currently, not all companies test their products, therefore, we cannot guarantee that all the products listed in our book are less than 20 ppm gluten.

Casein is the protein found in milk products. Milk is one of the top eight allergens recognized by the FDA. Products containing any form of milk have been excluded from this guide. This includes casein, caseinate, lactose, and any other milk derivative.

Soy is also one of the top eight allergens recognized by the FDA. Products containing any form of soy have been omitted from this guide, as well as soy lecithin and soybean oil.

Those products that have been manufactured in the same facility as gluten, casein or soy, but indicate that they thoroughly wash their lines between products have been included. We have tried our best not to include products from manufacturers that do not take measures to prevent cross-contamination.

For more information on our data collection and up to date product alerts, please visit our website www.CeceliasMarketplace.com.

Symbols

Certified/Tested Gluten-Free Products

&

Gluten-Free Facilities

There are some companies that manufacture their products in a dedicated gluten-free facility or environment. Some products also go through strict guidelines and vigorous testing by either the Celiac Sprue Association (CSA) Recognition Seal Program or the Gluten Intolerance Group (GIG) Gluten-Free Certification Organization to be verified as gluten-free. In this guide we have marked these manufacturers and products with the following symbols:

▲ - manufactured in a dedicated gluten-free facility or environment

● - verfied, tested, or certified gluten-free by either the CSA Recognition Seal Program or the GIG Gluten-Free Certification Organization

Celiac Sprue Association ®

Certified **GF** ™ Gluten-Free

This book is dedicated to:

All those in search of gluten/casein/soy free products.

Gluten/Casein/Soy Free Grocery Shopping Guide (A-Z)

A A

Almond Beverage... see Nut Beverages
Almonds... see Nuts
Amaranth
 Arrowhead Mills - Whole Grain
 Bob's Red Mill▲ - Organic Flour
 Nu-World Foods -
  Amaranth Side Serve (Garlic Herb●, Savory Herb●, Spanish Tomato●)
  Bread Crumbs●
  Flour●
  Pre Gel Powder●
  Puffed●
  Seed●
  Starch●
  Toasted Bran Flour●
Anchovies
 Crown Prince - Flat In Olive Oil, Rolled w/Capers In Olive Oil
 Crown Prince Natural - In Pure Olive Oil, Paste
Angel Hair Pasta... see Pasta
Animal Crackers... see Cookies
Apple Butter
 Eden Organic - Apple, Apple Cherry, Cherry
 Fischer & Wieser - Texas Pecan (Apple, Peach)
 Lucky Leaf
 Manischewitz
 Musselman's
Apple Cider... see Cider
Apple Cider Vinegar... see Vinegar
Apple Rings
 Lucky Leaf - Spiced
 Musselman's - Spiced

A

Apples... *All Fresh Apples Are Gluten/Casein/Soy Free*
   Lucky Leaf - Sliced
   Musselman's - Sliced

Applesauce
   Albertsons - Cinnamon, Natural, Original
   Apple Time - Natural
   Baxters - Bramley Apple Sauce
   Beech Nut Baby Food - Applesauce (Stage I Fruits, Stage 2 Fruits)
   Eden Organic -
      Organic Apple
         Cherry
         Cinnamon
         Regular
         Strawberry
   Food Club Brand - Applesauce (Chunky, Cinnamon, Mixed Berry, Natural, Original, Strawberry, Unsweetened)
   Full Circle - Organic (Cinnamon, Sweetened, Unsweetened)
   Great Value Brand (Wal-Mart) -
      Applesauce Glass Jar (Cinnamon, Regular, Unsweetened)
      Applesauce Plastic Cups (Cinnamon, Natural, No Sugar Added, Regular)
      Canned Applesauce Regular
   Hannaford Brand - Cinnamon, Original, Unsweetened
   Home Harvest Brand - Natural, Regular
   Hy-Vee - Applesauce, Cinnamon, Light w/(Mixed Berry, Strawberry), Natural
   Kroger Brand - Plain
   Lucky Leaf - Cinnamon, Natural, Regular
   Meijer Brand - Chunky, Cinnamon, Mixed Berry, Natural, Organic (Cinnamon, Sweetened, Unsweetened), Original, Regular, Strawberry

A

Midwest Country Fare - Home Style, Natural, w/(Cinnamon, Peaches, Raspberries, Strawberries)

Momma's Old Fashioned Applesauce - Original Flavor

Mott's - All Varieties

Musselman's - Chunky, Cinnamon (Lite, Regular), Golden Delicious, Granny Smith, Healthy Picks (Blueberry Pomegranate, Cupuacu Key Lime, Raspberry Acai), Homestyle (Cinnamon, Regular), Lite Fruit 'N Sauce (Cherry, Grape, Orange Mango, Peach, Raspberry, Strawberry), McIntosh Apple, Organic (Regular, Unsweetened), Regular, Sesame Street (Cherry), Totally Fruit (Apple, Peach, Strawberry), Unsweetened

Nature's Goodness Baby Food - Applesauce (Stage I, Stage 2)

O Organics

Publix - Chunky, Cinnamon, GreenWise Organic Unsweetened, Old Fashioned, Unsweetened

Safeway Brand - Cups, Natural, Sweetened

Spartan Brand - Cinnamon, Natural, Peach, Raspberry, Regular, Strawberry

Stop & Shop Brand - Applesauce (Chunky, Cinnamon, Mixed Berry, Natural, Strawberry)

Trader Joe's - Chunky Spiced Apples

Wegmans Brand -

Applesauce (Chunky, Cinnamon, McIntosh, Mixed Berry, No Sugar Added, Peach Mango, Regular)

Natural Applesauce No Sugar Added

Sweetened Applesauce

Winn Dixie - Cinnamon, Sweetened, Unsweetened

Woodstock Farms - Organic Applesauce (Apricot, Blueberry, Cinnamon, Mango, Raspberry, Regular)

Apricots... *All Fresh Apricots Are Gluten/Casein/Soy Free*

Albertsons - Canned

Del Monte -

Canned/Jarred Fruit (All Varieties)

Fruit Snack Cups (Metal, Plastic)

A

Food Club Brand - Canned Unpeeled Apricot Halves

Hy-Vee - Unpeeled Halves

Meijer Brand - Halves Unpeeled In Pear Juice

Publix - Canned Halves Unpeeled (In Heavy Syrup, Water & Artificial Sweetener)

S&W - All Canned/Jarred Fruits

Stop & Shop Brand - Heavy Syrup, Island Apricots In Light Syrup, Splenda

Winn Dixie - Unpeeled Halves In Heavy Syrup

Artichokes... *All Fresh Artichokes Are Gluten/Casein/Soy Free*

Native Forest - Artichoke Hearts (Marinated, Quartered, Whole)

Reese - Artichokes (Regular)

S&W - All Plain Canned Artichokes

Safeway Select - Marinated Artichoke

Spartan Brand - Artichoke Hearts (Plain)

Trader Joe's - Artichoke Hearts In Water

Wegmans Brand - Artichoke Hearts (Halves & Quarters, In Brine, Marinated Quartered), Marinated Long Stemmed

Winn Dixie - Artichoke Hearts

Asparagus... *All Fresh Asparagus Is Gluten/Casein/Soy Free*

Albertsons - Cuts & Tips, No Salt Spears, Whole Spears

Birds Eye - All Plain Frozen Asparagus

Cascadian Farm - Organic Frozen Asparagus Cuts

Del Monte - All Plain Canned Asparagus

Food Club Brand - Canned Whole Asparagus

Great Value Brand (Wal-Mart) - Canned (Cut Spears, Extra Long)

Green Giant - Canned Spears, Cut Asparagus

Hannaford Brand - Cuts & Tips, Whole Tall

Hy-Vee - Cut Spears

Kroger Brand - All Plain Asparagus (Canned, Frozen)

A

Laura Lynn - Cut Asparagus

Meijer Brand - Canned Cuts & Tips

B

Native Forest - Green (Cuts & Tips, Spears), White

Nature's Promise - Organic Asparagus Spears

S&W - All Plain Canned Asparagus

Safeway Brand - Canned Cut

Spartan Brand - Cut

Stop & Shop Brand - Asparagus (Spears, Tips & Cuts)

Trader Joe's - All Plain Frozen Asparagus

Wegmans Brand - Cleaned And Cut Tips, Cut Spears & Tips

Woodstock Farms - Organic Frozen Whole Baby Asparagus

Avocado... *All Fresh Avocados Are **Gluten/Casein/Soy Free***

Avocado Dip... see Guacamole and/or Dip/Dip Mix

B

Baby Food

Beech-Nut -

Cereal (Rice)

Stage 1 Fruits (Applesauce, Chiquita Bananas, Peaches, Pears)

Stage 1 Meats (Beef & Beef Broth, Chicken & Chicken Broth, Turkey & Turkey Broth)

Stage 1 Vegetables (Butternut Squash, Tender Golden Sweet Potatoes, Tender Sweet Carrots, Tender Sweet Peas, Tender Young Green Beans)

Stage 2 Desserts (DHA Plus Apple Delight)

Stage 2 Dinners (Apples & Chicken, Chicken & Rice, Chicken Noodle, Homestyle Chicken Soup, Macaroni & Beef w/Vegetables, Pineapple Glazed Ham, Sweet Potatoes & Chicken, Turkey & Rice, Vegetables & Beef, Vegetables & Chicken)

Stage 2 Fruits (Apples & Bananas, Apples & Blueberries, Apples & Cherries, Apples w/Mango & Kiwi, Apples w/Pears & Bananas, Applesauce, Apricots w/Pears & Apples, Chiquita Bananas,

B

Chiquita Bananas & Strawberries, DHA Plus Apple Delight, DHA Plus Apple w/Pomegranate Juice, DHA Plus Banana Supreme, Guava, Mango, Papaya, Peaches, Peaches & Bananas, Pears, Pears & Pineapples, Pears & Raspberries, Plums w/Apples & Pears)

Stage 2 Rice Cereal (Apples w/Cinnamon)

Stage 2 Vegetables (Butternut Squash, Carrots & Peas, Corn & Sweet Potatoes, Country Garden Vegetables, DHA Plus Butternut Squash w/Corn, DHA Plus Garden Vegetable, DHA Plus Sweet Potatoes, Mixed Vegetables, Sweet Corn Casserole, Sweet Potatoes & Apples, Tender (Sweet Carrots, Sweet Peas, Young Green Beans), Tender Golden Sweet Potatoes

Stage 3 Dinners (Country Vegetables & Chicken)

Stage 3 Fruits (Apples & Bananas, Chiquita Bananas, Homestyle Apples Cherries Plums, Homestyle Cinnamon Raisins & Pears, Homestyle Peaches Apples & Bananas, Homestyle Pears & Blueberries)

Stage 3 Rice Cereal & Pears

Stage 3 Turkey Rice Dinner

Stage 3 Vegetables (Green Beans & Corn & Rice, Sweet Potatoes)

Earth's Best Organic Baby Food -

1st Beginner First Foods (Apples, Bananas, Carrots, Pears, Peas, Sweet Potatoes)

2nd Antioxidant Blends (Apple Butternut Squash, Banana Mango, Carrot Tomato, Sweet Potato Apricot)

2nd Dinners (Chicken & Brown Rice, Rice & Lentil, Summer Vegetable, Sweet Potatoes & Chicken)

2nd Fruits (Apples, Apples & Apricots, Apples & Bananas, Apples & Blueberries, Apples & Plums, Bananas, Bananas & Peaches & Raspberries, Pears, Pears & Mangos, Pears & Raspberries, Plum Banana Brown Rice Fruit & Whole Grain Combinations)

2nd Gourmet Meals (Chicken Mango Risotto, Creamy Chicken Apple Compote, Sweet Pea Turkey & Wild Rice)

B

2nd Seasonal Harvest Blends (Sweet Potato Cinnamon, Pumpkin Apple)

2nd Vegetables (Carrots, Corn & Butternut Squash, Garden Vegetables, Green Beans & Rice, Peas & Brown Rice, Sweet Potatoes, Winter Squash)

3rd Dinners (Vegetable Beef Pilaf)

3rd Fruits (Banana & Strawberries, Chunky Orchard Fruit)

Whole Grain Rice Cereal

Gerber Baby Food -

1st Foods Fruits & Vegetables (Applesauce, Bananas, Carrots, Green Beans, Peaches, Pears, Peas, Prunes, Squash, Sweet Potatoes)

2nd Foods Desserts (Banana Yogurt, Fruit Medley)

2nd Foods Dinners (Apples & Chicken, Beef & Beef Gravy, Chicken & Chicken Gravy, Chicken & Rice, Ham & Ham Gravy, Pears & Chicken, Sweet Potatoes & Turkey, Turkey & Turkey Gravy, Veal & Veal Gravy, Vegetable Beef, Vegetable Chicken)

2nd Foods Fruits & Vegetables (Apple Blueberry, Apple Strawberry Banana, Apples & Cherries, Applesauce, Apricots w/Mixed Fruit, Banana Mixed Berry, Banana Orange Medley, Banana Plum Grape, Banana w/Apples & Pears, Bananas, Carrot Apple Mango, Carrots, Garden Vegetable, Green Beans, Mango, Mixed Vegetables, Peaches, Pear Pineapples, Pears, Peas, Prunes w/Apples, Smoothies (Hawaiian Delight, Peach Cobbler), Squash, Sweet Potatoes, Sweet Potatoes & Corn)

3rd Foods Desserts (Fruit Medley Dessert)

3rd Foods Dinners Vegetable (Beef, Chicken, Turkey)

3rd Foods Fruits & Vegetables (Applesauce, Banana Strawberry, Bananas, Carrots, Green Beans w/Rice, Peaches, Pears, Squash, Sweet Potatoes)

DHA (Apple Blackberry, Apples & Summer Peaches, Banana Mango, Banana Pineapple Orange Medley, Butternut Squash & Harvest Apples, Farmers Market Vegetable Blend)

Graduates For Toddlers (White Turkey Stew w/Rice & Vegetables)

Graduates Fruit (Diced Apples, Diced Peaches)

B

Graduates Fruit Strips (Apple, Strawberry, Wildberry)

Graduates Fruit Twists (Apple & Strawberry, Strawberry & Grape)

Graduates Juice Treats (Fruit Medley, Tropical)

Gerber Organic Baby Food -

1st Foods (Applesauce, Bananas, Carrots, Pears, Sweet Peas, Sweet Potatoes)

2nd Foods (Apple Strawberry, Applesauce, Bananas, Pear & Wildberry, Sweet Potatoes)

Mini Fruits - Apple, Banana Pineapple, Banana Strawberry

Homemade Baby - Baby Tex Mex●, Just (Apples●, Green Beans●, Pears●, Peas●, Squash●, Sweet Potatoes●), Piwi●, Squapples●, Yummy Yammies●

Meijer Brand -

Gluco Burst Arctic Cherry

Little Fruit (Apple, Strawberry Banana)

Little Veggies Corn

Nature's Goodness Baby Food -

Stage 1 Fruits & Vegetables (Applesauce, Bananas, Carrots, Green Beans, Peaches, Pears, Peas, Prunes, Squash, Sweet Potatoes)

Stage 2 Desserts (Banana Pudding, Cherry Vanilla Pudding, Dutch Apple, Fruit Dessert, Mango Fruit, Papaya Fruit, Tutti Frutti)

Stage 2 Dinners (Apples & Chicken, Apples & Ham, Broccoli & Chicken, Green Beans & Turkey, Sweet Potatoes & Turkey, Turkey Rice Dinner, Vegetable Dinner (Bacon, Beef, Chicken, Ham))

Stage 2 Fruits & Vegetables (Applesauce, Apples & Blueberries, Apples & Pears, Apples Strawberries & Bananas, Apples w/Squash, Apricots w/Pears & Apples, Bananas, Bananas w/Apples & Pears, Bananas w/Mixed Berries, Carrots, Corn & Sweet Potatoes, Green Beans, Mixed Vegetables, Peaches, Pears, Plums w/Apples, Prunes w/Pears, Pumpkins w/Pears, Squash, Sweet Peas, Sweet Potatoes)

Stage 2 Rice Cereal (& Peaches, w/Applesauce)

B

Stage 3 Desserts (Bananas & Strawberry w/Tapioca, Bananas w/Tapioca)

Stage 3 Dinners (Green Beans & Rice)

Stage 3 Vegetable Sweet Potatoes

O Organics -

Stage 1 (Applesauce, Bananas, Carrots, Peas, Sweet Potatoes)

Stage 2 (Apple Apricot, Apple Banana, Apple Wild Blueberry, Applesauce, Bananas, Carrots, Mixed Vegetables, Peach Rice Banana, Pear Raspberry, Pears, Peas & Brown Rice, Prunes, Squash, Sweet Potatoes, Summer Vegetables)

Stage 3 (Sweet Potato Chicken Dinner, Vegetable Beef Dinner, Vegetable Lentil Dinner)

Baby Formula

Hy-Vee - Pediatric Electrolyte (Fruit, Grape, Regular)

Neocate - Junior (Chocolate, Tropical, Unflavored), Nutra, One +

Bacon

Applegate Farms - Natural (Canadian, Dry Cured, Peppered, Sunday, Turkey), Organic (Sunday, Turkey)

Black Label

Butterball - Turkey (Lower Sodium, Regular, Thin & Crispy)

Dietz & Watson - Canadian Style

Farmer John - Premium Low Sodium, Quick Serve Fully Cooked

Garrett County Farms - Classic Sliced (Dry Rubbed, Turkey), Sliced (Applewood, Canadian Style), Thick Sliced Dry Rubbed, Turkey Peppered

Global Gourmet - Irish Bacon

Great Value Brand (Wal-Mart) - Hickory Smoked, Peppered, Turkey Bacon

Hannaford Brand - Maple, Sliced (Lower Sodium, Regular)

Honeysuckle White - Smoked Turkey Bacon

Hormel - Canadian Style, Fully Cooked, Microwave, Natural Choice (Canadian, Original)

Hy-Vee - Applewood, Double Smoked, Hickory, Hickory Smoked Fully Cooked, Lower Sodium, Maple, Peppered, Sweet Smoked

bacon bits

B

Jennie-O - Bacon (Extra Lean Turkey, Turkey)

Jimmy Dean - Premium Bacon (Hardwood Smoked Turkey, Lower Sodium, Original, Thick Slice)

Jones Dairy Farm -

Canadian●

Old Fashioned Slab Bacon●

Sliced (Cherrywood Smoked●, Regular●, Thick●)

Meijer Brand - Lower Sodium, Regular

Old Smokehouse - Applewood, Maple Peppered, Original

Oscar Mayer - America's Favorite, Center Cut, Hearty Thick Cut, Lower Sodium, Natural Smoked Uncured, Ready To Serve (Bacon, Thick Cut)

Publix - All Varieties

Safeway Brand - Hickory Smoked, Lower Sodium, Regular

Smithfield - Brown Sugar, Center Cut 40% Lower Fat, Cracked Peppercorn, Maple, Natural Hickory Smoked (Regular, Thick Sliced)

Wegmans - Fully Cooked Natural Smoked, Uncured Applewood Smoked

Wellshire Farms - Bulk Maple, Classic Sliced Dry Rubbed, Classic Sliced Turkey, Dry Rubbed Center Cut, Fully Cooked Hickory Smoked, Natural, Pa Pork Applewood Smoked, Sliced Beef, Sliced Canadian Brand Turkey, Sliced Canadian Style, Sliced Dry Rubbed, Sliced Maple, Sliced Pancetta, Sliced Peppered Dry Rubbed, Sliced Peppered Turkey, Thick Sliced Dry Rubbed, Whole Pancetta

Wellshire Organic - Organic (Dry Rubbed, Turkey)

Winn Dixie - Hickory Sweet Sliced Bacon (Lower Sodium, Regular, Thick, Thin)

Bacon Bits

Hormel - Bacon (Bits, Crumbles, Pieces)

Oscar Mayer - Real Bacon Bits

Publix - 100% Real Bacon Pieces

Wellshire Farms - Salt Cured Bacon Bits

B Bagels

    Enjoy Life▲ - Bagels (Cinnamon Raisin●, Classic Original●)

    Gluten-Free Creations▲ - Berry●, Cinnamon Raisin●, Everything●, Onion●, Plain●

    Kinnikinnick▲ - Tapioca Rice (Cinnamon Raisin, New York Style Plain, Sesame)

Baking Chips

    Ener-G▲ - Chocolate Chips

    Enjoy Life▲ - Semi Sweet Chocolate Chips●

Baking Cocoa

    Dagoba - Organic

    Hy-Vee

    Spartan Brand - Cocoa Baking Chocolate

Baking Decorations & Frostings

    Betty Crocker -

        Cookie Icing (Chocolate, Red, White)

        Decorating Decors Nonpareils

        Decorating Gels (All Colors)

        Decorating Icing (All Colors)

        Select Sugar Decors

    Cherrybrook Kitchen - Gluten Free Frosting (Chocolate, Vanilla) *(Box Must Say Gluten-Free)*, Ready To Spread Vanilla Frosting

    Edward & Sons - Let's Do...Sprinkelz (Carnival, Chocolatey, Confetti)

    Food-Tek Fast & Fresh - Dairy Free Chocolate Flavored Icing, Dairy Free Vanilla Flavored Icing

    Gluten-Free Creations▲ - Frosting Mix (Chocolate●, White●)

    Gluten-Free Essentials▲ - Frosting Mix (Lemon Glaze, Supreme Chocolate, Vanilla Royal)

    Kinnikinnick▲ - Icing Sugar

    Namaste Foods▲ - Chocolate Fudge, Toffee Vanilla

    Pamela's Products▲ - Frosting Mix (Confetti, Dark Chocolate, Vanilla)

Baking Mix... see Bread Mix

B

Baking Powder
  Barkat
  Bob's Red Mill▲
  Clabber Girl
  Davis
  El Peto▲ - Aluminum & Corn Free, Aluminum Free
  Ener-G▲ - Double Acting, Regular
  Glutino▲
  Hain Pure Foods
  Hannaford Brand
  Hearth Club
  Hy-Vee - Double Acting
  KC
  Kinnikinnick▲ - KinnActive
  Royal
  Rumford
  Spartan Brand
  Wegmans Brand - Double Acting
Baking Soda
  Albertsons
  Arm & Hammer
  Bob's Red Mill▲
  El Peto▲
  Ener-G▲ - Calcium Carbonate (Baking Soda Substitute)
  Hannaford Brand
  Hy-Vee
  Meijer Brand
  Spartan Brand
  Winn Dixie

B Banana Chips

    Brothers All Natural▲ - Crisps (Banana, Strawberry Banana)

    Woodstock Farms - Banana Chips (Regular, Sweetened)

Bananas... *All Fresh Bananas Are **Gluten/Casein/Soy Free***

    Chiquita

    Dole

    Woodstock Farms - Organic Frozen Bananas

Barbeque Sauce

    Bone Suckin' Sauce - Habanero, Original

    Cattlemen's - Classic, Smokehouse, Sweet & Spicy

    Daddy Sam's - Bar B Que Sawce (Ginger Jalapeno, Original)

    Fischer & Wieser - Plum Chipotle BBQ

    Hannaford Brand - Honey, Kansas City Style, Original, Sweet & Zesty

    Homestyle Meals - Original, Smoked Chipotle

    Hy-Vee - Hickory, Honey Smoke, Original

    Jack Daniels -

        Hickory Brown Sugar

        Honey Smokehouse

        Original No. 7 Recipe

    Kraft - Original Barbecue Sauce

    Midwest Country Fare - Hickory, Honey, Original

    Mr. Spice Organic - Honey BBQ

    Mrs. Renfro's - Barbecue Sauce

    Organicville - Organic BBQ Sauce (Original)

    Publix - Deli BBQ, Hickory, Honey, Original

    Safeway Select - Hickory Smoked, Honey (Mustard, Smoked), Original

    Saz's - Original, Sassy, Vidalia Onion

    Spartan Brand - Hickory & Brown Sugar, Honey, Original

    Sweet Baby Ray's - Hickory & Brown Sugar, Honey, Honey Chipotle, Hot 'N Spicy, Original, Sweet Vadalia Onion

    Walden Farms - Hickory Smoked, Honey, Original, Thick & Spicy

Wegmans Brand - Memphis Style, Tropical

Wild Thymes - Spicy Island BBQ Sauce

Winn Dixie - Hickory, Honey, Original

Bars... (includes Breakfast, Energy, Fruit, Protein, etc.)

Gluten Free▲ - Sweet Goodness Pan Bars●

Aller Energy Bars - Apple Cinnamon, Cherry Blossom, Chocolate Swirl, Wild Berry

Alpsnack -

Apricots & Cranberries

Coconut/Mango & Pineapple

Plums & Currants

Arico - Cookie Bars (Almond Cranberry, Lemon Ginger, Peanut Butter)

Boomi Bar -

Apricot Cashew

Cashew Almond

Cranberry Apple

Fruit & Nut

Healthy Hazel

Macadamia Paradise

Maple Pecan

Perfect Pumpkin

Pineapple Ginger

Pistachio Pineapple

Walnut Date

Bumble Bar - Awesome Apricot, Cherry Chocolate, Chocolate Crisp, Chunky Cherry, Original Flavor, Original Flavor w/(Almonds, Cashews, Hazelnuts, Mixed Nuts), Tasty Tropical

Clif Nectar - Organic (Cherry Pomegranate, Cranberry Apricot Almond, Dark Chocolate Walnut, Lemon Vanilla Cashew)

Dagoba - Conacado Dark Chocolate Bar

B

Eat Natural -
- 100% Organic Brazils Hazelnuts & Sultans
- Brazils Sultanas Almonds & Hazelnuts
- Dates Walnuts & Pumpkin Seeds
- Macadamias Brazils & Apricots
- Peanuts Almonds & Hazelnuts

Ener-G▲ - Chocolate Chip Snack Bar

Enjoy Life▲ - Boom Choco Boom (Crispy Rice●, Dark Chocolate●, Rice Milk●), Caramel Apple●, Cocoa Loco●, Sunbutter Crunch●, Very Berry●

Gopal's - Adam & Eve, Apple Delicious, Ayurvedic, Carob Quinoa, Country (All), Happy Herb w/Maca, Pineapple Nut, Pumpkin Agave, Rawmesan, Sesame Mango, Walnut Fig

Goraw - Bar (Banana Bread Flax●, Live Granola●, Live Pumpkin●, Real Live Flax●, Spirulina Energy●)

Jennies - Omega 3 Energy Bar (Coconut, Coconut Almond, Coconut Chocolate)

Larabar -
- Apple Pie●
- Banana Cookie●
- Cashew Cookie●
- Cherry Pie●
- Chocolate Coconut●
- Cinnamon Roll●
- Cocoa Mole●
- Coconut Cream Pie●
- Ginger Snap●
- Jocalat (Chocolate●, Chocolate Cherry●, Chocolate Hazelnut●, German Chocolate Cake●, Chocolate Coffee●, Chocolate Mint●)
- Key Lime Pie●
- Lemon Bar●

Peanut Butter & Jelly●

Peanut Butter Cookie●

Pecan Pie●

Pistachio●

Tropical Fruit Tart●

Mixes From The Heartland▲ - Coffee Bars (Apple Cinnamon●, Cinnamon●, Cranberry●, Tropical●)

Mrs. May's Naturals - Trio (Black Sesame Plus, Cranberry Crunch, Mango & Strawberry Plus)

Nonuttin' Foods▲ - Granola Bars (Apple Cinnamon, Chocolate Chip, Double Chocolate Chunk, Raisin)

NuGO Free - Gluten Free Bars (Carrot Cake●, Dark Chocolate Crunch●, Dark Chocolate Trail Mix●)

Nutiva Bars - Organic (Flax & Raisin, Hempseed Original)

Omega Smart Bars▲ - Banana Chocolate Chip, Pomegranate Strawberry Colada, Pumpkin Spice

Organic Food Bar -

Organic Food Bar (Active Greens, Chocolate Chip, Cranberry, Omega 3 Flax, Original, Protein, Vegan, Wild Blueberry)

Organic Food Bar Kids (Oohmega Cherry Pie, Oooatmeal Apple Pie, Keerunch Chocolate Brownie Crunch)

Oskri Organics -

Coconut Bar (Almond, Cherry, Mango, Original, Pineapple, Strawberry)

Date Fruit

Fig Fruit

Honey Bar (Cashew, Desert Date, Flaxseed, Granola, Mixed Nuts, Muesli, Turkish Delight)

Jalow (Almond Cranberry, Cashew Cranberry, Pecan Raisin)

Sesame Bar (Black Sesame, Date Syrup & (Black Cumin, Fennel, Regular), Molasses & (Black Cumin, Fennel, Regular), Quinoa)

B

Prana - Apple Pie, Apricot Goji, Apricot Pumpkin, Cashew Almond, Coconut Acai, Pear Ginseng

PURE Bar -

Organic

Apple Cinnamon

Cherry Cashew

ChocChip Trailmix

Chocolate Brownie

Cranberry Orange

Wild Blueberry

Ruth's Hemp Power -

Cranberry Trail HempPower

CranNut Flax Power

Ginger Almond MacaPower

VeryBerry Flax Power

Vote Hemp Blueberry Bar

Shakti Bar - Organic Blueberry Chia

thinkFruit - Apple Noni Nourish, Cashew Acai Protect, Chocolate Pomegranate Power, Peanut Goji Glow

thinkOrganic - Apricot Coconut, Cashew Pecan, Cherry Nut, Chocolate Coconut

Wegmans Brand - Fruit Flats (Cherry, Grape, Raspberry, Strawberry)

Basmati Rice... see Rice

Bean Dip... see Dip/Dip Mix

Beans... *All Fresh Beans Are Gluten/Casein/Soy Free (Except Soybeans)*

Albertsons - Refried Beans (Regular, Spicy, Vegetarian)

Amy's - Light In Sodium (Black, Traditional), Organic Refried Beans (Black, Traditional, w/Green Chiles), Vegetarian Baked

Arrowhead Mills - Adzuki, Anasazi, Garbanzo (Chickpeas), Green Split Peas, Lentils (Green, Red), Pinto

B&M Baked Beans - Baked Beans w/(Bacon & Onion, BBQ Flavored, Country Style, Maple Flavor, Original, Vegetarian), Red Kidney

beans

B

Birds Eye - All Plain Frozen Beans
Bush's Best -
> Baked Beans (Bold & Spicy, Boston Recipe, Country Style, Homestyle w/Bacon & Brown Sugar, Honey, Maple Cured Bacon, Onion, Original, Vegetarian)
>
> Black
>
> Butter (Baby, Large, Speckled)
>
> Cannellini
>
> Garbanzo
>
> Great Northern
>
> Grillin' Beans (Southern Pit Barbecue, Steakhouse Recipe)
>
> Kidney (Dark Red, Light Red)
>
> Navy
>
> Pinto
>
> Red

C & W - All Plain Frozen Beans *(Except Edamame/Soybeans)*
C R Darbell's - Pork & Beans
Cascadian Farms - Organic Frozen (Cut Green Beans, French Cut Green Beans w/Toasted Almonds, Petite Whole Green Beans)
Del Monte - All Plain Canned Beans *(Except Soybeans)*
Eden -
> Organic (Aduki, Baked w/Sorghum & Mustard, Black, Black Eyed Peas, Butter, Cannellini, Caribbean Black, Garbanzo, Great Northern, Kidney, Navy, Pinto, Small Red)
>
> Organic Dried (Aduki, Black, Garbanzo, Green (Lentils, Split Peas), Kidney, Navy, Pinto, Small Red)
>
> Refried (Black, Kidney, Pinto, Spicy Black, Spicy Pinto)
>
> Rice & (Cajun Small Red, Caribbean Black, Garbanzo, Kidney, Lentils, Pinto)

Fantastic World Foods - Hummus Original, Instant (Black, Refried)

B **Food Club Brand** - Frozen (Baby Lima, Cut Green, French Style Green, Whole Green)

Freshlike - All Frozen Plain Beans *(Except Edamame/Soybeans)*

Full Circle - Organic Frozen Cut Beans

Grand Selections -
   Fancy (Cut Green, Whole Green)
   Frozen Whole Green

Great Value Brand (Wal-Mart) - Dried Beans (Baby Lima, Black, Garbanzo, Great Northern, Large Lima, Light Red Kidney, Navy, Small Red)

Green Giant -
   Canned
      Cut Green (50% Less Sodium, Regular)
      French Style Green
      Kitchen Sliced Green
      Three Bean Salad
   Frozen
      Baby Lima
      Cut Green
      Green Beans & Almonds
      Select w/No Sauce Whole Green
      Simply Steam (Baby Lima No Sauce, Green Beans & Almonds)

Hannaford Brand - Black, Canned Great Northern, Cannellini, Cut Green, Cut Wax, Dark Red Kidney, French Green, Light Red Kidney, No Salt Cut, No Salt French, Pinto, Whole Green

Heinz - Vegetarian Beans

Home Harvest Brand - Canned Green (Cut, French Cut)

Hy-Vee -
   Black (Refried, Regular)
   Blue Lake (Cut Green, French Style Green, Whole Green)
   Butter

B

Country Style Baked
Dark Red Kidney
Dried (Baby Lima, Large Lima, Lentils, Mixed Soup, Navy)
Fat Free Refried
Frozen (Cut Green, French Cut Green)
Garbanzo Beans Chick Peas
Great Northern (Dried, Regular)
Home Style Baked
Light Red Kidney
Maple Cured Bacon Baked
Onion Baked
Original Baked
Pinto (Dried, Regular)
Pork & Beans
Red (Dried, Kidney, Regular)
Spicy Refried
Steam In A Bag Frozen Beans
Traditional Refried
Vegetarian Refried
Joan Of Arc - Black, Butter, Dark Red Kidney, Garbanzo, Great
  Northern, Light Red Kidney, Pinto, Red
Kid's Kitchen - Beans & Wieners
Kroger Brand - All Plain Beans *(Except Edamame/Soybeans)*
Laura Lynn -
  All Dried Beans *(Except Soybeans)*
  Canned (Kidney, Lima)
  Cut Green
  French Style Green
  No Salt Cut Green

B **Lowes Foods Brand** -
    Canned
        Black
        Cut Green No Salt
        French
        Garbanzo
        Great Northern
        Green (Cut, French Style, Whole)
        Lima
        Pinto
        Red Kidney Beans (Dark, Light)
        Whole Green
    Dry (Baby Lima, Black Eyed Peas, Great Northern, Lentil, Lima, Mixed, Navy, Pinto)
    Frozen
        Deluxe Whole Green
        Green (Cut, French Cut, Regular)
        Lima (Baby, Deluxe Tiny, Regular)
        Speckled Butter
Meijer Brand -
    Baked Beans (Organic)
    Canned Beans
        Black (Organic, Regular)
        Butter
        Garbanzo (Organic, Regular)
        Great Northern
        Lima
        Mexican Style
        Pinto (Organic, Regular)
        Red Kidney (Dark, Dark Organic, Light, Regular)
        Refried (Fat Free, Regular, Vegetarian)

B

      Refried Organic (Black Bean, Black Bean/Jalapeno, Roasted Chili/Lime, Traditional)

      Wax Cut

Canned Green Beans Cut

      Blue Lake

      French Style (Blue Lake, No Salt, Organic, Veri Green)

      No Salt

      Organic

      Veri Green

Canned Green Beans Whole

Dry Beans

      Black

      Blackeye

      Great Northern

      Green Split Beans & Peas

      Lentil

      Lima Large

      Navy

      Pinto

      Red Kidney

Frozen Green Beans (Cut, French Cut, Italian Cut)

Frozen Lima Beans (Baby, Fordhook)

Pork & Beans

Midwest Country Fare - Cut Green, French Style Green, Pork & Beans

Nielsen-Massey - Whole Vanilla Beans●

O Organics - Canned (Cut Green, Pinto), Frozen Whole Green

Old El Paso - Refried Beans (Fat Free, Spicy Fat Free, Traditional, w/Green Chiles)

Ortega - Refried (Fat Free, Regular)

Pictsweet - All Plain Frozen Beans *(Except Edamame/Soybeans)*

B   Publix -
   Canned
      Baked
      Black Beans (Frijoles Negros, In Seasoned Sauce)
      Garbanzo
      Great Northern
      Green (French Cut, French Style, Italian Cut, Lima, No Salt Added, Original, Veggi Green, Whole)
      Kidney (Dark, Light)
      Pinto
      Pork & Beans
   Dry
      Baby Lima
      Black
      Blackeye
      Garbanzo
      Great Northern
      Green Split Peas
      Large Lima
      Lentils
      Light Red Kidney
      Navy
      Pinto
      Small Red
   Frozen
      Butter
      Green (Cut, French Cut, Pole)
      Lima (Baby, Fordhook)
   Publix GreenWise Market - Organic Canned (Black, Dark Red Kidney, Garbanzo, Green, Pinto)
   S&W - All Plain Canned Beans *(Except Soybeans)*

Safeway Brand -
  Canned
    Black (Eyed, Regular)
    Chick
    Dark Kidney
    Green (Cut, Cut No Salt, French Style, Whole)
    Light Kidney
    Lima
    Pinto
  Dried
    Baby Lima
    Black (Eyed, Regular)
    Great Northern
    Green Split
    Large Lima
    Lentils
    Light Red Kidney
    Navy
    Pink
    Pinto
    Small (Red, White)
  Frozen (Baby Lima, Cut, Fordhook Lima, French Style, Whole)
  Refried Beans (Fat Free, Traditional)
Spartan Brand -
  Canned
    Baked (Regular, w/Bacon & Maple Flavor, w/Onions)
    Black
    Butter
    Dark Red Kidney
    Garbanzo
    Great Northern

B

Green (Cut, French Cut French Style)
Homestyle Baked
Light Red Kidney
Lima
Pinto
Pork & Beans
Red
Refried (Fat Free, Regular)
Wax
Whole Green
Dried
Black
Black Eyed
Great Northern
Kidney
Lentil
Lima (Baby, Large)
Navy
Pinto
Frozen
Baby Lima
Cut Green
French Cut Green
Whole Green
Stop & Shop Brand -
Baby Lima
Beans
Black
Dark Red Kidney
Fordhook Lima
Garbanzo

Green Beans (Cut, French, No Added Salt, Whole)

Kidney Light

Lima

Organic Green

Pinto

Thrifty Maid - Frozen Green Beans

Wegmans Brand -

Baby Lima

Baked Beans (Vegetarian)

Black

Butter

Canned (Black, Dark Red Kidney, Great Northern, Light Red Kidney, Pinto, Pork & Beans, Red)

Cannellini Beans

Cut Green Beans (No Salt, Regular)

Dark Kidney

French Style Green Beans (No Salt, Regular)

Garbanzo Beans Italian Classics

Great Northern

Green (Cut, French Style, Italian Cut, Regular, Whole)

Light Kidney

Lima

Pinto

Pork & Beans In Tomato Sauce

Wax Cut

Winn Dixie -

Canned

Black

Butter

Dark Red Kidney

Garbanzo

B

    Green No Salt Added
    Green Whole
    Light Red Kidney
    Pinto
  Dried
    Baby Lima
    Bean Soup Mix
    Garbanzo
    Great Northern
    Large Lima
    Lentils
    Light Red Kidney
    Navy
    Pinto
  Frozen Green Beans (Organic Cut, Whole)
  Frozen Lima Beans (Baby, Fordhook, Petite, Speckled)
  Organic Canned
    Black
    Dark Red Kidney
    Garbanzo
    Light Red Kidney
    Pinto
  Refried Beans (Fat Free, Traditional)
Woodstock Farms - Dried Green Beans, Organic Frozen (Baby French Beans, Cut Green Beans, Lima)

Beef... *All **Fresh** Meat Is **Gluten/Casein/Soy Free** (Non-Marinated, Unseasoned)*

Applegate Farms -
  Natural (Beef Hot Dogs, Roast Beef)
  Organic (Frozen Beef Burger, Roast Beef)

Carl Buddig -
　Deli Thin Sliced Beef
　Extra Thin Sliced Beef

Dietz & Watson -
　Corned Beef Brisket
　Corned Beef Flat (Extra Lean)
　Pastrami (Brisket, Spiced Beef)
　Roast Beef (Black Bear Choice, Cap Off ½, Italian, Natural
　　Angus, Oven Roasted All Natural Rare Whole)

Garrett County Farms -
　Beef Franks (4XL Big, Old Fashioned, Premium)
　Corned Beef Brisket (Half, Whole)

Great Value Brand (Wal-Mart) - Frozen 100% Pure Beef Patties

Hillshire Farms -
　Deli Select Thin Sliced (Corned Beef, Roast Beef)
　Deli Select Ultra Thin Roast Beef

Homestyle Meals - Shredded Beef In BBQ Sauce

Hormel -
　Corned Beef
　Corned Beef Hash
　Deli Sliced Cooked Corned Beef
　Dried Beef
　Natural Choice Roast Beef

Hy-Vee - Quarter Pounders, Thin Sliced (Regular)

Meijer Brand - Ground Beef (Chuck Fine, Fine)

Organic Prairie -
　Fresh Organic
　　Ground Beef 1lb. (85% Lean, 90% Lean)
　　Sliced Roast Beef 6 oz.

B

Frozen Organic
>> Beef Liver Steak 12 oz.
>> Ground Beef 12 oz.
>> Ground Beef Patties 10.6 oz.
>> New York Strip Steak 8 oz.
>> Ribeye Steak 8 oz.

Oscar Mayer - Shaved Deli Fresh (French Dip Roast Beef, Slow Roasted Roast Beef)

Primo Taglio - Cooked Corned Beef, Roast Beef (Caramel Color Added, Coated w/Seasonings)

Wellshire Farms - Roast Beef (Sliced Top Round, Whole)

Wellshire Organic - Organic Beef Franks

Winn Dixie - Corned Beef

Beef Jerky... see Jerky/Beef Sticks

Beef Sticks... see Jerky/Beef Sticks

Beer

AMERICAN

Anheuser-Busch - Redbridge Beer

Bard's Tale Beer - Dragon's Gold Gluten Free Lager

Lakefront Brewery - New Grist Beer

Old Hat Brewery - Bees Knees

Ramapo Valley Brewery - Passover Honey Lager

IMPORTED

Bi-Aglut - Special 76 Lager (Italy)

Brauerei Grieskirchen AG - Beer Up Glutenfrei Pale Ale (Austria)

Carlsberg Brewery - Saxon Premium Lager (Finland)

Fine Ale Club - Against The Grain (England)

Glutaner - Glutenfrei Pils (Belgium)

Green's - Discovery, Explorer, Herald, Pioneer, Trailblazer (England)

Hambleton Ales - GFA, GFL, Pale (England)

Koff - Lager, Taytelainen Kevytolut (Finland)

Laitilan - Kukko Pils III Lager, Kukko Tumma III Dark Lager (Finland)

Les Bieres de la Nouvelle France - La Messagere Pale Ale (Canada)

Liebhart's Privatbrauerai - Bio Reis Gold, Bio Reis Gold Dunkel (Germany)

O'Brien - Brown Ale, Pale Ale, Premium Lager (Australia)

Schnitzer Brau - Glutenfrei Bier (Germany)

Silly Yaks - Aztec Gold (Australia)

St. Peter's Brewery G Free (England)

Beets... *All Fresh Beets Are Gluten/Casein/Soy Free*

Del Monte - All Plain Canned Beets

Food Club Brand - Canned (Sliced, Whole)

Hannaford Brand - Cut, Sliced, Whole

Hy-Vee - Fancy (Diced, Sliced)

Laura Lynn - Cut, Sliced

Lowes Foods Brand - Cut, Whole

Meijer Brand -
  Harvard Sweet Sour,
  Sliced (No Salt, Pickled, Regular)
  Whole (Medium, Pickled)

Publix - Canned

Safeway Brand - Canned (Sliced, Whole)

Spartan Brand - Diced, Sliced, Whole

Stop & Shop Brand - Sliced No Salt Added

Wegmans Brand -
  Harvard, Sliced (No Salt, Pickled, Regular)
  Whole (Pickled, Regular)

B Berries... *All **Fresh** Berries Are **Gluten/Casein/Soy Free***

   Cascadian Farm - Organic Frozen Harvest Berries

   Del Monte -

      Canned/Jarred Fruit (All Varieties)

      Fruit Snack Cups (Metal, Plastic)

   Great Value Brand (Wal-Mart) - Frozen

   Meijer Brand - Frozen Berry Medley, Frozen Triple Berry Blend

   Publix - Frozen Mixed Berries

   Spartan Brand - Frozen Berry Medley

   Stop & Shop Brand - Frozen Berry Medley

   Wegmans Brand - Berry Medley

   Woodstock Farms - Organic Frozen Mixed Berries

Beverages... see **Drinks/Juice**

Biscotti

   Ener-G▲ - Chocolate Chip

   Foods By George▲ - Currants Nut & Seed

   Orgran▲ - Amaretti, Classic Chocolate

   Sorella▲ - Biscottines (Chocolate Almond, Cinnamon Swirl, Hazelnut Anise, Vanilla)

Biscuits

   1-2-3 Gluten Free▲ - Southern Glory Biscuits●

   Bob's Red Mill▲ - Wheat Free Biscuit & Baking Mix

   Cause You're Special▲ - Hearty Gluten Free Biscuit Mix

   Mixes From The Heartland▲ -

      Biscuit Mix

      Country●

      Dilly●

      Garlic●

      Roasted Pepper●

      Sun Dried Tomato●

B

    Namaste Foods▲ - Biscuits Piecrust & More Mix
    The Really Great Food Company▲ - Biscuit Mix (Loaf, Old Time)
Bittermelon... *All Fresh Bittermelon Is Gluten/Casein/Soy Free*
Black Eyed Peas... see Peas
Blackberries... *All Fresh Blackberries Are Gluten/Casein/Soy Free*
   Albertsons - All Frozen Fruit
   Cascadian Farm - Organic Frozen
   Food Club Brand
   Great Value Brand (Wal-Mart) - Frozen
   Meijer Brand - Frozen
   Publix - Frozen
   Safeway Brand - Frozen
   Spartan Brand - Frozen
   Stop & Shop Brand - Frozen
   Trader Joe's - Plain Frozen
   Wegmans Brand
   Winn Dixie - Frozen
   Woodstock Farms - Organic Frozen
Blueberries... *All Fresh Blueberries Are Gluten/Casein/Soy Free*
   Albertsons - All Frozen Fruit
   Cascadian Farm - Organic Frozen
   Food Club Brand - Frozen
   Full Circle - Organic Blueberries
   Great Value Brand (Wal-Mart) - Frozen
   Hy-Vee - Frozen
   Kroger Brand - Plain Frozen Fruit
   Meijer Brand - Frozen (Organic, Regular)
   Publix - Frozen
   Safeway Brand - Frozen
   Spartan Brand - Frozen

B   Trader Joe's - Plain Frozen
    Wegmans Brand
    Winn Dixie - Frozen
    Woodstock Farms - Organic Frozen Wild

Bok Choy... *All Fresh Bok Choy Is Gluten/Casein/Soy Free*

Bologna
    Applegate Farms - Turkey Bologna
    Honeysuckle White - Turkey
    Hy-Vee - German Brand
    Midwest Country Fare - Sliced, Thick Sliced
    Publix - Deli Pre Pack Sliced Lunch Meat (Beef Bologna, German Bologna)
    Shelton's - Uncured Turkey
    Wellshire Farms - Sliced Beef Bologna

Bouillon/Bouillon Cubes
    Better Than Bouillon - Chili Base, Organic (Beef, Chicken), Reduced Sodium Chicken
    Celifibr - Bouillon Cubes (Vegetable Medley, Vegetarian Beef, Vegetarian Chicken), Bouillon Soup Base (French Onion Vegetable Medley, Vegetarian Beef, Vegetarian Chicken)
    Edward & Sons - Garden Veggie, Low Sodium Veggie, Not Beef, Not Chick'n
    Harvest Sun - Organic Bouillon Cubes (All Flavors)
    Herb-Ox - Low Sodium (Beef, Chicken)
    Lee Kum Kee - Chicken Bouillon Powder
    Massel - Ultracubes (Beef, Chicken, Vegetable)
    Spartan Brand - Soup Chicken Bouillon (Granular)

Bourbon... *All Distilled Alcohol Is Gluten/Casein/Soy Free* [2]

Bowls
    Amy's - Cream Of Rice Hot Cereal
    Chi-Chi's - Fiesta Plates Salsa Chicken

Lundberg▲ - Organic Brown Rice Bowls (Country Wild, Long Grain, Short Grain)

B

Bratwurst... see Sausage

Bread... (includes Rolls)

  Apple's Bakery▲ - Loaf (Olive Oil)

  Aunt Gussie's▲ - Kalamata Garlic Bread, Rosemary Focaccia

  El Peto▲ -

    Bread

      Flax Seed Loaf

      Millet

      Multi Grain

      Potato

      Raisin

      Tapioca

      White Rice

    Rolls

      Brown

      Multi Grain

      White

  Ener-G▲ -

    Sliced Breads

      Brown Rice

      Cinnamon Rolls

      Corn

      Egg Free Raisin

      Four Flour

      Hi Fiber

      Light (Brown Rice, Tapioca, White Rice, White Rice Flax)

      Papas

      Raisin Loaf w/Eggs

B

    Rice Starch
    Seattle Brown
    Tapioca Loaf (Dinner Rolls, Regular Sliced, Thin Sliced)
    White (Regular, Rice Flax)
    Yeast Free (Brown Rice, Sweet, White Rice)
  Specialty Breads
    Bread Crumbs
    Broken Melba Toast
    Communion Wafers
    Plain Croutons

Food For Life -
  Almond Rice
  Bhutanese Red Rice
  Brown Rice
  Multi Seed Rice
  Raisin Pecan
  Rice Pecan
  White Rice

French Meadow Bakery - Gluten Free (Italian Rolls●, Sandwich Bread●)

Gluten Free Life▲ -
  Country Brown Pure
  Multi Grain Pure
  Pumperknickle

Gluten-Free Creations▲ - Almond Flax●, Herb Baguettes●, Herb Loaf Bread●, Herb Rolls●, Honey Oat●, Hot Dog Buns●, Rye Bread w/Caraway Seeds●, Seeded Multigrain●, White●, Whole Grain●, Wild Rice●

Katz Gluten Free▲ -
  Bread (Whole Grain)
  Chocolate (Rugelech, Strip)
  Cinnamon (Rugelech, Strip)

B

Farfel
Honey Loaf
Kiska Kugel
Rolls (Sandwich)
Kinnikinnick▲ -
Brown Sandwich
Candida Yeast Free Multigrain Rice
Festive
Many Wonder Multigrain Rice
Robins Honey Brown Rice
Sunflower Flax Rice
Tapioca Rice (Italian, Raisin, Regular, Yeast Free)
Tru Fibre Multigrain Rice
White Sandwich
Namaste Foods▲ - Bread Mix
Nu-World Foods -
Flatbread Amaranth
Buckwheat●
Garbanzo●
Sorghum●
Orgran▲ - Crisp Bites (Balsamic Herb, Corn, Onion & Chives),
Crisp Bread (Corn, Rice, Rice & Cracked Pepper, Rice & Garden
Herb, Salsa)
Rose's Bakery▲ -
French (Bread●, Rolls●)
Millet●
Sandwich●
Seeded Sandwich●
Teff●
Schar▲ - Classic White Rolls

B Bread Mix... (includes Baking Mix)

1-2-3 Gluten Free▲ - Aaron's Favorite Rolls●

Arrowhead Mills - All Purpose Baking Mix

Authentic Foods▲ - Cinnamon Bread Mix, Wholesome Bread Mix

Bob's Red Mill▲ - Bread Mix (Cinnamon Raisin)

Breads From Anna▲ - Bread Mix (All Purpose, Banana, Classic Herb, Original Dairy Free, Pumpkin)

Chebe▲ -

Bread Mix (All Purpose●, Cinnamon Rolls●, Focaccia Italian Flatbread●, Pizza Crust●)

Garlic Onion Breadsticks Mix●

El Peto▲ - Bread Mix (Potato, White)

Ener-G▲ - Mix (Corn, Potato, Rice)

Fearn - Baking Mix (Brown Rice, Rice)

Gillian's Foods▲ - All Purpose Baking Mix

Gluten-Free Creations▲ - Break Mix (Almond Flax●, Cinnamon Raisin●, Honey Oat●, Seeded Multigrain●)

Gluten-Free Essentials▲ - All Purpose Baking Mix, Holiday Gingerbread, Lemon Poppy Seed, Multi Grain (Cinnamon Spice, Meatloaf Starter, Original, Zesty Italian)

Gluten-Free Pantry▲ - Toms Light Gluten Free Bread

Kinnikinnick▲ -

All Purpose Mix

Candida Yeast Free Rice

Tapioca Rice

White Rice

Mixes From The Heartland▲ - Bread Machine Mix (Garden Veggie●, Garlic Roasted Pepper●, Plain●), Corn Bread Mix●, Sweet Bread Mix (Banana●, Blueberry●, Cranberry●, Zucchini●)

Namaste Foods▲ - Bread Mix

Orgran▲ - Bread Mix (Alternative Grain Wholemeal, Easy Bake)

Pamela's Products▲ - Amazing Bread Mix

Schar▲ - Classic White Bread Mix

Simply Organic - Banana●, Chai Spice Scone Mix●

The Really Great Food Company▲ - Bread Mix (Brown Rice, Dark European, French/Country Farm, Home Style Cornbread, Irish Soda, Old Fashioned Cinnamon, Original White, Rye Style)

Breadcrumbs... see Coating

Breadsticks

Chebe▲ - Garlic & Onion Breadsticks Mix●

Glutino▲ -

Pizza Breadsticks

Sesame Breadsticks

Schar▲ - Italian Breadsticks

Breakfast

Dietz & Watson - Breakfast Ham Slices w/Water Added

Honeysuckle White - Breakfast Turkey Sausage (Links, Patties)

Ian's - Wheat Free Gluten Free Recipe French Toast Sticks

Jennie-O Turkey Store -

Fresh Breakfast Sausage (Mild Links, Mild Patties)

Johnsonville -

Original Breakfast (Links, Patties)

Vermont Maple Syrup (Links, Patties)

Jones Dairy Farm -

All Natural

Hearty Pork Sausage Links●

Light Pork Sausage and Rice Links●

Little Link Pork Sausage●

Maple Sausage Patties●

Original Pork Roll Sausage●

Pork Sausage Patties●

All Natural Golden Brown Cooked & Browned Sausage Patties (Maple Fully●, Mild Fully●)

B

All Natural Golden Brown Fully Cooked & Browned Turkey●

All Natural Golden Brown Light Fully Cooked & Browned Sausage & Rice Links●

All Natural Golden Fully Cooked & Browned Sausage Links (Made From Beef●, Maple●, Mild●, Spicy●)

Only Oats - Breakfast Blend (Apple & Cinnamon●, Maple & Roasted Flax●)

Sunshine Burger - Organic Breakfast Patty

Broccoli... *All Fresh Broccoli Is Gluten/Casein/Soy Free*

Albertsons - Canned & Frozen

Birds Eye - All Plain Frozen Broccoli

C & W - All Plain Frozen Broccoli

Cascadian Farm - Organic Frozen (Broccoli Cuts, Broccoli Florets), Purely Steam Organic Frozen Broccoli & Carrots

Food Club Brand - Frozen (Chopped, Cut)

Freshlike - Frozen Plain Broccoli

Green Giant - Frozen Chopped

Home Harvest Brand - Cuts

Hy-Vee - Frozen (Chopped, Cuts, Florets)

Kroger Brand - All Plain Broccoli (Canned, Frozen)

Lowes Foods Brand - Frozen (Chopped, Cuts, Deluxe Baby Florets, Deluxe Florets, Spears)

Meijer Brand - Frozen (Chopped, Cuts, Spears)

Midwest Country Fare - Frozen (Chopped, Cuts)

Nature's Promise - Organic Broccoli Mini Spears

Pictsweet - All Plain Frozen Broccoli

Publix - Frozen (Chopped, Cuts, Florets, Spears)

Safeway Brand - Frozen (Cuts, Florets, Steam In Bag)

Spartan Brand - Cuts, Florets

Stop & Shop Brand - Broccoli (Chopped, Cuts, Spears), Broccoli & Cauliflower

Trader Joe's - All Plain Frozen Broccoli

Wegmans Brand - Broccoli (Chopped, Cuts), Broccoli Cuts & Cauliflower Florets, Spears

Winn Dixie - Frozen (Chopped, Cuts, Florets, Spears), Steamable Broccoli Cut

Woodstock Farms - Organic Frozen Broccoli Florets

Broth

Baxters - Chicken

College Inn - Garden Vegetable

Health Valley -

Fat Free

Beef Flavored (No Salt Added, Regular)

Chicken

Vegetable

Low Fat Chicken (No Salt Added, Regular)

Imagine - Organic Beef (Low Sodium, Regular), Organic Free Range Chicken (Low Sodium, Regular), Organic No Chicken, Organic Vegetable (Low Sodium, Regular)

Meijer Brand -

Naturals Broth

Carton (Beef, Chicken, Vegetable)

Concentrate (Beef, Chicken, Turkey)

Pacific Natural Foods - Beef Broth, Free Range Chicken, Organic (Beef, Free Range Chicken, Low Sodium Chicken, Low Sodium Vegetable, Mushroom, Vegetable Broth)

Safeway Brand - Beef, Chicken (Fat Free Reduced Sodium)

Shelton's -

Chicken (Fat Free Low Sodium, Regular)

Organic (Chicken, Chicken Fat Free Low Sodium)

Spartan Brand - Beef

Swanson -

Chicken Broth (Canned)

Natural Goodness Chicken Broth (Canned, Carton)

Vegetarian Broth (Canned)

B Winn Dixie -
    Resealable Broth Boxes
      Beef (Fat Free)
      Chicken (Fat Free, Organic Fat Free, Reduced Sodium)
      Vegetable (Organic Fat Free)

Brown Sugar... see Sugar

Brownies/Brownie Mix
    1-2-3 Gluten Free▲ - Divinely Decadent Brownies●
    Bob's Red Mill▲ - Gluten Free Brownie Mix
    El Peto▲ - Brownie Mix
    Ener-G▲ - Brownies
    Foods By George▲ - Brownies
    French Meadow Bakery - Gluten Free Fudge Brownie Bites●
    Gillian's Foods▲ - Brownie Mix, Brownies
    Gluten Free Life▲ - The Ultimate Gluten Free Cake Muffin &
      Brownie Mix
    Gluten-Free Creations▲ - Rich Brownie Mix●
    Hol Grain - Chocolate Brownie Mix
    Mixes From The Heartland▲ - Sweet Potato Brownie Mix●
    Namaste Foods▲ - Brownie Mix
    Rose's Bakery▲ - Chocolate Brownies●
    The Really Great Food Company▲ - Aunt Tootsie's Brownie Mix

Bruschetta
    Classico - Basil & Tomato, Extra Garlic
    Santa Barbara
    Tassos - Mediterranean

Brussel Sprouts... *All Fresh Brussel Sprouts Are Gluten/Casein/*
    Soy Free
    Birds Eye - All Plain Frozen Brussel Sprouts
    C & W - All Plain Frozen Brussel Sprouts
    Food Club Brand - Frozen

Hy-Vee - Frozen
Lowes Brands Foods - Frozen (Deluxe Baby, Regular)
Meijer Brand - Frozen
Midwest Country Fare - Frozen
Pictsweet - All Plain Frozen Brussel Sprouts
Publix - Frozen
Stop & Shop Brand
Spartan Brand - Frozen
Trader Joe's - All Plain Frozen Brussel Sprouts
Wegmans Brand - Frozen (Regular)
Winn Dixie - Frozen

Buckwheat
  Arrowhead Mills
  Bob's Red Mill▲ - Organic Buckwheat (Groats, Kasha)
Buckwheat Bread... see Bread
Buckwheat Groats
  Arrowhead Mills
  Bob's Red Mill▲ - Organic Buckwheat Groats
Buffalo Wing Sauce... see Wing Sauce
Buffalo Wings... see Wings
Buns
  Cybro's - Gluten Free Rice Rolls
  El Peto▲ -
    Hamburger Buns (Millet, Multigrain, Potato, Tapioca, White)
    Hot Dog Buns (Millet, Potato, White Rice)
  Ener-G▲ -
    Hamburger Buns (Brown Rice, Seattle Brown, Tapioca, White Rice)
    Hot Dog Buns (Seattle Brown, Tapioca)
  Gluten-Free Creations▲ - Hamburger Buns (Regular●, White●), Hot
    Dog Buns●

B   **Kinnikinnick▲** - Tapioca Rice Buns (Cinnamon, Hamburger Buns, Hot Cross, Hot Dog, Multigrain Seed & Fibre, Tray)

C   **Quejos** - Buns (Dairy Free Quejos)

    Schar▲ - Classic White Rolls

Burgers... *All **Fresh** Ground Meat Is **Gluten/Casein/Soy Free** (**Non-Marinated, Unseasoned**)*

    Applegate Farms - Organic (Beef, Turkey)

    Butterball - Turkey Burgers (All Natural, Seasoned)

    Honeysuckle White - Fresh Ground Turkey Patties, Frozen Turkey Burgers

    Jennie-O Turkey Store- Fresh Lean Turkey Burger Patties (Regular, Seasoned), Frozen All Natural Turkey Burgers

    Organic Prairie - Frozen Organic Ground Beef Patties 10.6 oz.

    Shelton's - Turkey

    Sunshine Burgers - Organic (Barbecue, Breakfast, Falafel, Garden Herb, Original, South West)

    Wellshire Farms - All Natural Frozen (Beef Hamburgers, Turkey Burgers)

    Winn Dixie - Frozen Angus Beef Patties (Original, w/Grill Seasoning, w/Sweet Onion)

Butter... see also Spread

    Earth Balance - Natural Buttery Spread (Soy Free)

    Eden Organic - Apple, Apple Cherry, Montmorency Tart Cherry

    Manischewitz - Apple Butter

    Odell's - Clarified Butter, Popcorn Butter, Seafood Butter

    Purity Farms - Organic Ghee (Clarified Butter)

C

Cabbage... *All **Fresh** Cabbage Is **Gluten/Casein/Soy Free***

Cake/Cake Mix

    1-2-3 Gluten Free▲ - Delightfully Gratifying Bundt Poundcake●, Peri's Perfect Chocolate Bundt Poundcake●, Yummy Yellow Cake Mix●

C

Authentic Foods▲ - Cake Mix (Chocolate, Devil's Food Chocolate, Lemon, Vanilla)

Bob's Red Mill▲ - Chocolate Cake Mix

Cause You're Special▲ - Golden Pound, Moist (Lemon, Yellow), Rich Chocolate

Cherrybrook Kitchen - Gluten Free Chocolate Cake Mix *(Box Must Say Gluten-Free)*

Ener-G▲ - Poundcake

Food-Tek Fast & Fresh - Cake Mix Dairy Free Minute (Chocolate, Cinnamon Coffee, White Cake, Yellow Cake)

Gifts Of Nature▲ - Cake Mix (Yellow)

Gluten Free Life▲ - The Ultimate Gluten Free Cake Muffin & Brownie Mix

Gluten-Free Creations▲ - Yellow Cake●, Yellow Cupcakes●, Winkies●

Gluten-Free Essentials▲ -

Mix (Extreme Chocolate Cake, Holiday Gingerbread, Spice Cake & Muffin, Yellow Velvet Cake)

Speedy Bake Mix (Chocolate Mud, Spice Is Nice, Yella Vanilla)

Hodgson Mill▲ - Gluten Free Chocolate Cake Mix, Gluten Free Yellow Cake Mix, Multi Purpose Baking Mix

Jo-Sef▲ - Brownie Roll, Jelly Roll

Katz Gluten Free▲ - Cup Cakes (Chocolate, Vanilla)

Kinnikinnick▲ - Angel Food, Chocolate, Fruit, Sponge, White

Laurel's Sweet Treats▲ - Cake Mix (Cinnamon Spice, Morris Chocolate, Vanilla)

Madwoman Foods▲ - Tea Cakes (Banana Chocolate, Banana Cinnamon, Blueberry Chocolate Cherry, Cocoa Mocha, Lemon Blueberry, Lemon Poppyseed, Orange Chocolate, Orange Cranberry, Pecan Cocoa Mocha)

Maggie's Gluten Free Goodies▲ - Scrumptious Chocolate Cake Mix

C

Mixes From The Heartland▲ - Cake Mix (Chocolate Angel Food●, Chocolate Poundcake●, Cinnamon Orange●, Lime Poundcake●, Raspberry Poundcake●, Strawberry Angel Food●, Strawberry Poundcake●, Upside Down●, Vanilla Angel Food●, Vanilla Poundcake●)

Namaste Foods▲ - Cake Mix (Chocolate, Spice, Vanilla)

Orgran▲ - Cake Mix (Chocolate, Vanilla)

Pamela's Products▲ - Cake Mix (Chocolate, Classic Vanilla)

Ruby Range - Gluten Free Baking Mix (Chocolate Truffle Cake & Cupcakes●, Spice Cake & Cupcakes●)

Simply Organic -

Banana Bread Mix●

Carrot Cake Mix●

Cocoa Cayenne Mix●

Honeypot Ginger●

Sofella - Gluten Free Chocolate Cake Mix & Frosting Mix●

The Cravings Place▲-

Cinnamon Crumble Coffeecake Mix

Dutch Chocolate Cake Mix

Raisin Spice Cookie & Cake Mix

The Really Great Food Company▲ - Cake Mix (Angel Food, Banana Bread, Chocolate, Chocolate Cupcake, Colonial Spice, Devil's Food, Gingerbread, Golden, Grandma's Pound, Lemon Poppy, Orange, Pineapple, Pumpkin Bread, Pumpkin Spice, White, Yellow)

Calamari... *All Fresh Seafood Is Gluten/Casein/Soy Free*

Candy/Candy Bars

Altoids - Large Tins (Peppermint, Wintergreen)

Candy Tree

Licorice

Black Licorice (Bites, Laces, Vines)

Cherry (Bites, Laces, Vines)

Raspberry (Bites, Laces, Vines)

Strawberry (Bites, Laces, Vines)

C

Lollipops
- Cherry
- Lemon
- Orange
- Raspberry
- Strawberry

Cherry Mash - Cherry Flavored Candy Bar

Dots - Crows, Fruit Flavors, Regular, Tropical

Fluff Stuff - Cotton Candy, Tear Jerkers

Gimbal's Fine Candies▲ - All Varieties

Great Value Brand (Wal-Mart) -
- Butterscotch Discs
- Cinnamon Discs
- Fruit Slices
- Gummy (Bears, Worms)
- Orange Slices
- Peppermints Starlight Mints
- Spearmint Starlight Mints
- Spice Drops

Haribo -
- Alphabet Letters
- Centipedes
- Clown Fish
- Fizzy Cola
- Frogs
- Fruit Salad
- Gold Bears
- Gummi Apples
- Happy Cola
- Mini Rainbow Frogs

C

Peaches
Pink Grapefruit
Raspberries
Rattle Snakes
Sour Cherries
Strawberries
Super Cola
Techno Bears
Twin Cherries

Hershey's - Jolly Ranchers (Hard Candy)

Hy-Vee -

Assorted Gum Balls
Butterscotch Buttons
Cinnamon Imperials
Circus Peanuts
Dum Dum Suckers
Gummi (Bears, Peach Rings, Worms)
Lemon Drops
Orange Slices
Smarties
Spice Drops
Starlight Mints
Wax Bottles

Let's Do...Organic - All Gummi Bears

Lifesavers - Original

Maple Grove Farms Of Vermont - Blended Maple, Pure Maple

Mars -

Skittles (All Varieties)
Starburst (All Varieties)

Nestle - Spree

Nik-L-Nip - Wax Bottles

Publix -
  Candy Corn
  Circus Peanuts
  Fruit Slices
  Gummi (Bears, Worms)
  Jelly Beans
  Orange Slices
  Pastel Mints
  Smarties Candy
  Spearmint Starlight Mints
  Spice Drops
  Starlight Mints Candy
  Sweet Stripes

Razzles - Gum (Regular, Sour, Tropical)

Safeway Brand - Dessert Mints, Gummi Bears, Gummi Worms, Lemon Drops, Orange Slices, Spice Drops, Star Light Mints

Sharkies ▲ - Energy Sports Chews (Berry Blast, Citrus Squeeze, Fruit Splash, Peach Tea Breeze, Watermelon Scream)

Skittles - All Varieties

Sour Patch Kids - All Varieties

Spangler - Candy Canes, Dum Dum Pops

St. Claire's Organics - All Candy, Mints, Sour Tarts

Starburst - All Varieties

Swedish Fish

The Ginger People - Ginger Chews

Wack-O-Wax - Wax Fangs, Wax Lips

Winn Dixie -
  Butterscotch Buttons
  Candy Corn
  Circus Peanuts
  Gummi Bears

C

Gummi Worms

Jelly Beans

Orange Slices

Peach Rings

Sour Worms

Spice Drops

Starlight Mints

Wonka -

Bottlecaps

Gobstoppers (Original)

Lik M Aid Fun Dip

Nerds (Regular)

Pixy Stix

Runts (Original)

Sweet Tarts

Woodstock Farms - Vegetarian (Jelly Pebbles, Gummy Cubs)

Canned Chicken

Hormel - Chunk Meats (Breast Of Chicken)

Meijer Brand - Chicken Chunk White

Member's Mark - Premium Chunk

Sweet Sue - Boned Chicken Breast

Winn Dixie - Chicken Breast In Water

Canned Ham

Black Label - Canned Hams

Hormel - Chunk Ham Meat

SPAM - Classic, Less Sodium, Lite, Oven Roasted Turkey, Smoke Flavored

Underwood - Deviled Ham

Canned Salmon... see Fish

Canned Tuna... see Tuna

C

Canned Turkey
   Hormel - Chunk Turkey Meat
   SPAM - Oven Roasted Turkey
Canola Oil... see Oil
Capers
   B&G - Spanish Style Capote
   Wegmans Brand - Italian Classics (Capote, Nonpareil)
Cappuccino... see Coffee
Carbonated Beverage... see Soda Pop/Carbonated Beverages
Carrots... *All Fresh Carrots Are Gluten/Casein/Soy Free*
   Albertsons - Canned, Frozen
   Birds Eye - All Plain Frozen Carrots
   C & W - All Plain Frozen Carrots
   Del Monte - All Plain Canned Carrots
   Food Club Brand - Canned Sliced, Crinkle Cut, Whole Baby
   Freshlike - All Frozen Plain Carrots
   Grand Selections - Frozen Whole Carrots
   Great Value Brand (Wal-Mart) - Canned Sliced Carrots
   Hannaford Brand - Sliced, Whole Baby
   Hy-Vee -
      California
      Classic Cut & Peeled Baby
      Frozen Crinkle Cut
      Sliced
   Kroger Brand - All Plain Carrots (Canned, Frozen)
   Laura Lynn - Sliced Carrots, Whole Baby Carrots
   Lowes Foods Brand - Deluxe Whole Baby, Peas & Carrots, Sliced
   Meijer Brand - Canned Sliced (No Salt, Regular), Frozen Carrots
      (Crinkle Cut, Whole Baby)
   Midwest Country Fare - Sliced Carrots

C

Pictsweet - All Plain Frozen Carrots

Publix - Canned Carrots, Frozen (Crinkle Cut, Peas & Carrots, Whole Baby)

Publix GreenWise Market - Organic (Baby, Carrots, Chips, Juicing, Shredds, Snack)

S&W - All Plain Canned Carrots

Safeway Brand - Sliced Carrots

Spartan Brand - Canned (Peas & Sliced Carrots, Sliced), Frozen (Crinkle Cut, Peas & Carrots, Whole Baby)

Stop & Shop Brand - Carrots

Trader Joe's - All Plain Frozen Carrots

Wegmans Brand - Baby Cut, Carrots/Potatoes/Celery & Onions, Crinkle Cut, Organic, Sliced Carrots (No Salt Added, Regular), Whole Style

Winn Dixie - Frozen (Crinkle Cut, Whole Baby)

Cashews... see Nuts

Cauliflower... *All Fresh Cauliflower Is Gluten/Casein/Soy Free*

Albertsons - Canned & Frozen

Birds Eye - All Plain Frozen Cauliflower

C & W - All Plain Frozen Cauliflower

Freshlike - All Frozen Plain Cauliflower

Hy-Vee - Frozen Cauliflower Florets

Lowes Foods Brand - Frozen Cauliflower

Meijer Brand - Frozen Cauliflower Florets

Midwest Country Fare - Frozen Cauliflower

Pictsweet - All Plain Frozen Cauliflower

Publix - Frozen

Safeway Brand - Frozen

Spartan Brand - Frozen Florets

Trader Joe's - All Plain Frozen Cauliflower

Wegmans Brand - Florets

Winn Dixie - Frozen

Caviar

Romanoff - Black (Lumpfish, Whitefish), Red (Lumpfish, Salmon)

Celery... *All Fresh Celery Is **Gluten/Casein/Soy Free***

Celery Salt... see Seasonings

Cereal

Amy's - Cream Of Rice Hot Cereal Bowl

Ancient Harvest Quinoa - Quinoa Flakes

B & G - Cream Of Rice Hot Cereal

Bakery On Main - Gluten Free Granola (Apple Raisin Walnut, Cranberry Orange Cashew, Extreme Fruit & Nut, Nutty Maple Cranberry, Rainforest)

Barbara's Bakery - Multigrain Puffins, Organic Brown Rice Crisps, Organic Corn Flakes

Bob's Red Mill▲ - Creamy Rice Hot Cereal (Organic, Regular), Flaxseed Meal, Gluten Free Mighty Tasty Hot, Organic Creamy Buckwheat

Eat Natural - For Breakfast (Gluten Free Toasted Buckwheat Pumpkin Seeds Raisins & Mango, Gluten Free Raisins Almonds Mixed Seeds & Crispy Rice)

Eco-Planet - 7 Whole Grains Hot Cereal (Apples & Cinnamon●, Maple & Brown Sugar, Original●)

El Peto▲ - Apple Cinnamon Cream Of Rice, Cream Of Brown Rice, Cream Of White Rice, Unsweetened Corn Flakes

Ener-G▲ - Rice Bran

Enjoy Life▲ - Granola Crunch (Cinnamon●, Cranapple●, Very Berry●)

Erewhon -

    Aztec Crunchy Corn & Amaranth

    Brown Rice Cream

    Corn Flakes

    Crispy Brown Rice (Cocoa, Gluten Free Regular, w/Mixed Berries)

    Rice Twice

    Strawberry Crisp

C **General Mills▲** - Chex (Corn, Honey Nut, Rice)

Glutano▲ - Cornflakes, Pops

Gluten Free Sensations - Cream Of Brown Rice, Granola (Cherry Vanilla Almond, Cranberry Pecan, French Vanilla Almond)

Glutenfreeda▲ - Instant Oatmeal (Apple, Banana Maple, Cinnamon, Maple Raisin)

Health Valley - Blue Corn Flakes, Corn Crunch Ems, Rice Crunch Ems

Kinnikinnick▲ - Kinni Crisp Rice Cereal, Rice Bran

Lundberg▲ - Hot 'N Creamy Purely Organic Rice

Meijer Brand - Grits (Quick)

Montana Monster Munchies - Whole Grain Oat Bran●

Nature's Path -

    Envirokidz Organic

      Amazon Frosted Flakes

    Nature's Path Organic

      Crispy Rice

      Honey'd Corn Flakes

      Mesa Sunrise

      Whole O's

New Morning - Cocoa Crispy Rice

Nu-World Foods -

    Amaranth Berry Delicious●

    Amaranth O's (Original●, Peach●)

    Cereal Snaps (Cinnamon●, Cocoa●, Original●)

    Puffed Amaranth Cereal●

Orgran▲ - Multigrain O w/Quinoa

Perky's - Apple Cinnamon O's●, Frosted O's●, Nutty Flax●, Nutty Rice●, Original O's●

Pocono - Cream Of Buckwheat

Seitenbacher - Whole Grain Cornflakes, Musli #7

Wegmans Brand - Fruity Rice Crisps

C

Chamomile Tea... see Tea

Champagne...
   All Champagne **Made In USA Is **Gluten/Casein/Soy Free*** [2]

Cheese
   Eat In The Raw - Parma Vegan Parmesan (Chipotle Cayenne, Original)
   Galaxy Nutritional Foods - Rice Vegan (Slices) *(Must Say 'Vegan')*
   Gopal's - Rawmesan
   Road's End Organics - Organic (GF Alfredo Chreese Mix, GF Cheddar Chreese Mix)
   The Vegetarian Express - Parma Zaan Sprinkles

Cherries... **All **Fresh** Cherries Are **Gluten/Casein/Soy Free***
   Cascadian Farm - Organic Frozen Sweet Cherries
   Food Club Brand - Frozen Dark Sweet Cherries
   Great Value Brand (Wal-Mart) - Maraschino
   Hy-Vee - Frozen Cherry Berry Blend, Red Maraschino Cherries (Regular, w/Stems)
   Lucky Leaf - Red Tart Pitted Cherries
   Meijer Brand - Frozen (Dark Sweet, Tart), Maraschino Cherry (Red, Red w/Stems)
   Midwest Country Fare - Maraschino Cherries
   Musselman's - Red Tart Pitted Cherries
   Publix - Frozen Cherries (Dark Sweet), Maraschino
   S&W - All Canned/Jarred Fruits
   Safeway Brand - Frozen Dark Sweet Cherries, Maraschino Cherries
   Spartan Brand - Frozen Dark Sweet Cherries, Maraschino Cherries (Green, Red, Red w/Stems, Salad)
   Stop & Shop Brand - Dark Sweet Cherries
   Thrifty Maid - Maraschino Cherries
   Traverse Bay Fruit Co. - Premium Dried Cherries
   Wegmans Brand - Maraschino (Jumbo w/out Stems, w/Stems, w/out Stems), Sweet, Triple Cherry Fruit Mix In Light Syrup

C   **Winn Dixie** - Dark Sweet Cherries, Maraschino Cherries

Woodstock Farms - Organic Frozen Dark Sweet Cherries

Cherries Jubilee

   Lucky Leaf

   Musselman's

Chewing Gum

   B Fresh - All Varieties

   Bazooka

   Glee

   Nicorette - Fresh Mint, Fruit Chill, White Ice Mint

Chick Peas... see Beans

Chicken... *All Fresh Chicken Is **Gluten/Casein/Soy Free (Non-Marinated, Unseasoned)***

   Applegate Farms - Organic (Roasted Chicken Breast, Smoked Chicken Breast)

   Bakers & Chefs - Canned All Natural Chicken Breast

   Bell & Evans - Gluten Free Grilled Chicken Breasts (Regular)

   Butterball - Thin Sliced Oven Roasted Chicken Breast

   Carl Buddig - Deli Thin Sliced Chicken

   Chi-Chi's - Fiesta Plates (Chicken Salsa)

   Dinty Moore - Microwave Meal (Rice w/Chicken)

   Empire Kosher - Chicken Bologna Slices, Organic (Breasts, Drumsticks), Rendered Chicken Fat

   Farmer John - California Natural Chicken Sausage (Apple Chicken Smoked, Cajun Style Smoked, Chicken Brat Smoked, Lemon Cracked Pepper Chicken Smoked, Mango & Habanero Smoked)

   Garrett County Farms - Chicken Franks, Frozen Chicken Apple Breakfast Links

   Gillian's Foods ▲ - Chicken Cutlets

   Hannaford Brand - Chicken Breast Chunk In Water

   Hillshire Farms - Deli Select Thin Sliced Oven Roasted Chicken Breast

   Homestyle Meals - Shredded Chicken In BBQ Sauce

chicken

C

Honeysuckle White - Chicken Breast Deli Meat (Oil Browned)

Hormel - Chunk Meats (Breast Of Chicken, Chicken), Natural Choice (Grilled Carved Chicken Breast, Oven Roasted Carved Chicken)

Ian's - Wheat Free Gluten Free Recipe (Chicken Finger Kids Meal, Chicken Nuggets, Chicken Patties)

Jennie-O - Deli Chicken Breast (Mesquite Smoked)

John Soules Foods -
Ready To-Cook (Chicken Breast For Fajitas, Chicken Thigh For Fajitas)

Meijer Brand - Canned Chicken Chunk White in Water, Frozen Boneless Skinless Chicken (Breast Tenders, Breast w/Rib Meat, Thigh, Wing)

Member's Mark - Canned Premium Chunk Chicken Breast

Organic Prairie -
Fresh Organic
Sliced Roast Chicken Breast 6 oz.
Frozen Organic
Boneless Skinless Chicken Breasts
Chicken Italian Sausage 12 oz.
Ground Chicken 12 oz.
Whole Young Chicken

Oscar Mayer -
Deli Fresh Oven Roasted Chicken Breast
Shaved Deli Fresh (Cajun Seasoned Chicken Breast, Rotisserie Style Chicken Breast)
Thin Sliced Deli Fresh Oven Roasted Chicken Breast

Perdue - Rotisserie Oven Stuffer Roaster Breast

Saz's - Barbecue Chicken Meat Tub

S'Better Farms▲ - Chicken (Ballontine, Fingers, Party Wings, Siciliano, Szechwan)

C

Shelton's - Capon, Free Range (Breasts, Thighs, Whole), Organic (Boneless/Skinless Breast, Breast, Cut Up, Whole Chicken, Whole Legs)

Spartan Brand - Chicken Breast Chunk, Frozen Boneless Skinless (Breasts, Tenders)

Sweet Sue - Premium Chicken Breast Pouch

Tyson Simply Perfect -

100% All Natural Fresh Chicken

Boneless

Chicken Breast Tenders

Skinless (Chicken Breasts, Split Chicken Breasts)

Thin & Fancy Chicken Breasts

Valley Fresh - 100% Natural (Premium White Chicken, White & Dark Chicken)

Wellshire Farms - Chicken Franks, Sliced Oven Roasted Chicken Breast

Wellshire Organic - Organic Chicken Franks

Chicken Broth... see Broth

Chicken Nuggets... see Chicken

Chicken Wings... see Wings

Chiles

Chi-Chi's - Green Chiles

La Victoria - Green Chiles (Diced, Whole)

Meijer Brand - Diced Mild Mexican Style

Old El Paso - Green Chiles (Chopped, Whole)

Safeway Brand - Diced Green

Spartan Brand - Green Chiles

Chili

Amy's - Organic Chili (Black Bean, Medium w/Vegetables), Southwestern Black Bean

Hormel - Chili Master (Chipotle Chicken No Bean, Chipotle Chicken w/Beans), Chili w/Beans (Chunky, Hot, Regular)

Hy-Vee - Hot Chili w/Beans, Mild w/Beans

Kettle Cuisine - Angus Beef Steak Chili w/Beans●, Three Bean Chili●

Meijer Brand - Chili (No Beans Regular, w/Beans Regular)

Mimi's Gourmet - Black Bean & Corn, Spicy White Bean & Jalapeno, Three Bean w/Rice

Shelton's - Mild Chicken, Mild Turkey, Spicy Chicken, Spicy Turkey

Stagg -

Classic

Ranch House Chicken

Silverado Beef

Steak House

Winn Dixie - Chili w/Beans

Chili Powder

Chugwater Chili

Durkee

McCormick

Meijer Brand

Spartan Brand

Spice Islands

Tone's

Chili Sauce

A Taste Of Thai - Garlic Chili Pepper Sauce, Sweet Red Chili Sauce

Frank's RedHot - Chile 'N Lime

Hannaford Brand

Heinz

La Victoria - Red

Las Palmas - Red Chile

Lee Kum Kee - Sriracha Chili

Meijer Brand - Hot Dog Chili

C
   Safeway Brand
   Thai Kitchen - Spicy Thai, Sweet Red
   Wegmans Brand
   Winn Dixie - Sweet

Chips
   Boulder Canyon Natural Foods -
      Canyon Cut Potato Chips
         Totally Natural
      Kettle Cooked Potato Chips
         50% Reduced Salt
         Balsamic Vinegar & Rosemary
         Limon
         Sea Salt & Cracked Pepper
         Tomato & Basil
         Totally Natural
      Rice & Adzuki Bean Snack Chips
         Natural Salt
   Brothers All Natural▲ - Potato Crisps (Black Pepper & Sea Salt, Fresh Onion & Garlic, Original w/Sea Salt, Szechuan Pepper & Fresh Chives)
   Cape Cod -
      Potato
         40% Reduced Fat
         Classic
         Robust Russet
         Sea Salt & Vinegar
         Sweet Mesquite Barbeque
   Deep River Snacks -
      Mesquite BBQ
      Original Salted

Reduced Fat Original Salted

Salt & Cracked Pepper

Sweet Maui Onion

Eden - Brown Rice

Food Should Taste Good - Tortilla Chips (Buffalo●, Chocolate●, Cinnamon●, Jalapeno●, Lime●, Olive●, Potato & Chive●, Sweet Potato●, The Works!●, Yellow Corn●)

Fritos -

Corn Chips (Original, Scoops)

Glenny's - Spud Delites Natural Potato Crisps (Sea Salt, Texas BBQ)

Goraw - Super Chips (Pumpkin●, Spirulina●)

Hannaford Brand - Tortilla Chips (White Bite Size, Yellow Rounds)

Herr's -

Potato Chips

Crisp 'N Tasty

Honey BBQ

Ketchup

Lightly Salted

Mesquite BBQ Kettle

No Salt

Old (Bay, Fashioned)

Red Hot

Ripple

Tortilla/Corn Chips

Bite Size Dippers

Regular Corn Chips

Restaurant Style

Hy-Vee -

Baked Chips (Original)

Potato Chips (No Salt, Original)

C **Kettle Brand** -
  Baked Potato Chips
    Hickory Honey Barbeque
    Lightly Salted
    Salt & Fresh Ground Pepper
    Sea Salt & Vinegar
  Krinkle Cut Potato Chips
    Classic Barbeque
    Lightly Salted
    Salt & Fresh Ground Pepper
  Organic Potato Chips
    Chipotle Chili Barbeque
    Lightly Salted
    Sea Salt & Black Pepper
  Potato Chips
    Backyard Barbeque
    Death Valley Chipotle
    Honey Dijon
    Jalapeno
    Lightly Salted
    Salt & Fresh Ground Pepper
    Sea Salt & Vinegar
    Spicy Thai
    Unsalted
  Tortilla Chips
    Black Bean
    Blue Corn
    Chili Lime
    Yellow Corn

Lay's -
  Potato Chips
    Classic
    Deli Style Original
    Kettle Cooked (Original)
    Light Original
    Lightly Salted
    Natural (Sea Salt Thick Cut)
  Wavy Potato Chips
    Original
Lundberg▲ -
  Rice Chips
    Honey Dijon
    Pico de Gallo
    Santa Fe Barbecue
    Sea Salt
    Wasabi
Maui Style - Potato Chips (Regular)
Michael Season's -
  Baked Multigrain Chips (Honey Chipotle, Original)
  Thin & Crispy (Honey Barbecue, Lightly Salted, Ripple, Salt & Pepper, Unsalted)
Miguel's - Tortilla Chips (Blue Corn●, White Corn●)
Miss Vickie's -
  Kettle Cooked Potato Chips
    Simply Sea Salt
    Smokehouse BBQ
Mr. Krispers -
  Baked Rice Krisps (Sea Salt & Pepper●)
  Multi Seed Chips (Original●)

C

O Organics - Tortilla Chips (Blue w/Flax Seed, Blue w/Sesame, White, Yellow)

Old Dutch - Potato Chips (Ketchup, Original)

Pinnacle Gold -
Natural Baked Potato Chips Original
Natural Baked Veggie Chips

Pringles - Fat Free (Original)

Publix GreenWise Market - Tortilla Chips (Blue, Yellow)

RiceWorks -
Rice Crisps
Sea Salt
Salsa Fresca
Sweet Chili

Ruffles -
Potato Chips
Natural Reduced Fat Sea Salted
Original (Light, Reduced Fat, Regular)

Snyder's Of Hanover -
Corn Tortilla Chips (Restaurant Style, White, Yellow)
Potato Chips (Barbeque, Original, Ripple Potato)

Solea -
Olive Oil Chips
Cracked Pepper
Rosemary
Sea Salt
Polenta Chips (Sea Salt)

Spartan Brand - Potato (Regular, Ripple)

Tostitos -
Tortilla Chips
Light Restaurant Style
Natural Corn Restaurant Style (Blue, Yellow)

C

UTZ -

All Natural Kettle Cooked
    Dark Russet
    Gourmet Medley
    Lightly Salted

Grandma

Home Style Kettle Cooked Plain

Kettle Classics
    Dark Russet
    Plain
    Sweet Potato

Kettle Cooked (Barbeque, Plain)

Mystic Kettle Cooked Chips
    Dark Russet
    Plain
    Sea Salt & Vinegar

Regular Chips
    Barbeque
    Crab
    Honey BBQ
    No Salt Regular
    Plain (Flat, Ripple, Wavy Cut)
    Red Hot
    Reduced Fat

Tortilla Chips
    Baked

Wegmans Brand -

Corn

Kettle (Original)

Original Potato

Tortilla 100% White Corn (Blue Corn, Yellow Corn)

Wavy

C

Winn Dixie -
> Potato Chips
>> Classic
>> No Salt
>> Salt & Vinegar
>> Wavy

Wise -
> Corn Chips (BBQ Flavored Dipsy Doodles, Dipsy Doodles Rippled)
> New York Deli (Jalapeno Flavored, Kettle Cooked)
> Potato Chips (Flat Cut, Lightly Salted, Unsalted, Wise Wavy)
> Ridgies
> Tortilla Chips Bravos! (Restaurant Style, White Round)

Woodstock Farms - Veggie Chips

Chocolate
> **Earth Source Organics -** Organic Raw Chocolate Bar (Acai●, Caramel●, Goji●, Maca●)

> **Manischewitz -** Coconut Tenders, Peppermint Patties, Swiss Mints

Chocolate Bars... see also Chocolate
> **Enjoy Life▲ -** Boom Choco Boom (Crispy Rice●, Dark Chocolate●, Rice Milk●)

Chocolate Chips... see Baking Chips

Chocolate Syrup... see Syrup

Chole
> **Tamarind Tree -** Alu Chole

Chutney
> **Baxters -**
>> Albert's Victorian
>> Crushed Pineapple & Sweet Pepper
>> Spiced Fruit

C

    Spicy Mango

    Tomato

Hannaford Brand - Mango Chutney

Native Forest - Chutney (All Varieties)

Patak's - Chutney (Hot Mango, Major Grey, Sweet Mango)

Sharwood's - Green Label (Mango, Mango Chilli, Smooth)

Wild Thymes - Apricot Cranberry Walnut, Caribbean Peach Lime, Mango Papaya, Plum Currant Ginger

Cider

    Doc's Draft - Apple, Pear, Raspberry *(Alcoholic)*

    Safeway Brand - Apple Cider

    Sonoma Sparkler - Natural (Peach, Pear, Raspberry), Organic (Apple, Lemonade)

    Woodchuck▲ - Draft Ciders (All Styles) *(Alcoholic)*

    Wyder's - All Styles *(Alcoholic)*

Cinnamon

    Durkee

    McCormick

    Spice Islands

    Tone's

Cinnamon Rolls

    Kinnikinnick▲ - Tapioca Rice Cinnamon Buns

Clams... **All Fresh Seafood Is Gluten/Casein/Soy Free (Non-Marinated, Unseasoned)*

    Bumble Bee - Chopped, Fancy Smoked, Fancy Whole Baby, Minced

    Chicken Of The Sea - Minced, Whole Baby Clams

    Crown Prince -

        Natural (Boiled Baby Clams, Clam Juice, Smoked Baby Clams In Olive Oil)

        Regular (Baby Boiled, Chopped, Clam Juice, Minced)

    Ocean Prince - Chopped

C Club Soda... see Soda Pop/Carbonated Beverages
Coating
  Ener-G▲ - Breadcrumbs
  Gillian's Foods▲ - Breadcrumbs (Cajun Style, Italian Style, Plain)
  Gluten-Free Essentials▲ - Breading & Batter Mix (Seasoned, Unseasoned)
  Hol Grain - Brown Rice Bread Crumbs, Crispy Chicken Coating Mix
  Katz Gluten Free▲ - Bread Crumbs
  Kinnikinnick▲ - Graham Style Cracker Crumbs
  Nu-world Foods - Amaranth Bread Crumbs●
  Orgran▲ - All Purpose Crumbs, Corn Crispy Crumbs
  Southern Homestyle - Corn Flake Crumbs, Tortilla Crumbs
Cocktail Mix
  Holland House -
    Daiquiri
    Manhattan
    Pina Colada
    Strawberry Daiquiri Margarita
    Sweet & Sour Mix
  Margaritaville - Margarita Mix
  Mr. & Mrs. T's -
    Mai Tai
    Margarita
    Pina Colada
    Strawberry Daiquiri Margarita
    Sweet & Sour
    Whiskey Sour
  Rose's - Grenadine, Infusions (Blue Raspberry, Cranberry Twist, Sour Apple), Mojito (Mango, Passion Fruit, Traditional), Sweetened Lime Juice

C

Cocktail Sauce... see also Seafood Sauce

   Frontera - Cocktail & Ceviche Sauce (Cilantro Lime, Tomato Chipotle)

   Hannaford Brand - Cocktail Sauce

   Lou's Famous - Cocktail Sauce

   McCormick -

      Extra Hot

      Gold Dip (Regular)

      Original

      Seafood Sauce (Cajun Style, Mediterranean, Santa Fe Style)

   Publix - Seafood Cocktail Sauce

   Texas Pete - Seafood Cocktail

   Walden Farms

Cocoa Mix/Powder

   Dagoba - Authentic Hot Chocolate, Chocolate Syrup, Organic Cacao Powder, Unsweetened Hot Chocolate, Xocolatl Hot Chocolate

   Ghirardelli - White Mocha

   Hershey's - Chocolate Syrup (Lite, Regular, Special Dark), Cocoa (Special Dark, Unsweetened Regular)

   Shiloh Farms - Cocoa Powder

Coconut

   Baker's - Coconut (Bags, Cans)

   Food Club - Sweetened Coconut

   Great Value Brand (Wal-Mart) - Sweetened Flaked Coconut

   Hy-Vee - Flake Coconut

   Kroger Brand - Regular, Sweetened

   Laura Lynn

   Let's Do...Organic - Creamed, Flakes, Shredded (Reduced Fat, Regular, Unsweetened)

   Lowes Foods Brand - Flakes

C

Publix - Coconut Flakes

Safeway Brand - Coconut (Sweetened)

Spartan Brand - Coconut Flakes

Wegmans Brand - Sweetened Flakes

Winn Dixie - Coconut

Woodstock Farms - Coconut Medium Shred

Coconut Milk

A Taste Of Thai - Coconut Milk (Lite, Regular)

Native Forest - Organic Coconut Milk (Light, Regular)

So Delicious - Original●, Unsweetened●, Vanilla●

Thai Kitchen - Thailand (Lite, Lite Organic, Premium, Premium Organic)

Cod... see Fish... *All Fresh Fish Is Gluten/Casein/Soy Free (Non-Marinated, Unseasoned)*

Coffee

Brown Gold - All Varieties

Folger's - Classic (Decaf, Regular)

Food Club Brand - Ground Coffee (Classic Roast, Columbian, Decaf, French Roast, Lite Classic Roast)

Full Circle - Organic (Espresso Blend Ground, French Roast, Ground, Guatamalan Reserve Ground, Morning Blend Ground, Morning Blend Whole Bean, Signature Blend Ground)

Great Value Brand (Wal-Mart) -

100% Arabica Premium (Ground Coffee, Instant Coffee)

100% Colombian Premium Ground Coffee (Naturally Decaf, Regular)

French Roast - 100% Arabica Premium Ground Coffee

Naturally Decaf Premium Instant Coffee

Hannaford Brand - Columbian, Decaf Premium, House Blend, Light Columbian Instant, Premium Blend

Hy-Vee -

100% Colombian

Breakfast Blend

Classic Blend

coffee

C

    Classic Decaf

    Coffee (Instant, Regular)

    Decaf (Instant, Regular)

    French Roast

Kroger Brand - Unflavored (Ground, Instant, Whole)

Laura Lynn - All Coffee Beans

Lowes Foods Brand -

    Bag (100% Colombian (Decaf, Regular), French Roast, Signature Blend)

    Brick (100% Colombian, Decaf, French Roast, Lite, Regular)

    Can (Regular)

    Instant (Decaf, Regular)

    Singles (Microwaveable)

Maxwell House -

    Coffee Bags (Decaf, Master Blend, Regular)

    Ground (Breakfast Blend, Dark Roast, Hazelnut, Original, Slow Roast, Vanilla)

    Filter Packs & Singles (Decaf, Original)

    Instant (Decaf, Reduced Caffeine/Lite, Original)

Meijer Brand - Decaf, French Roast, Ground (Colombian, French Roast, Lite 50% Decaf), Regular

Midwest Country Fare - Classic Blend

Millstone - All Coffee Beans, All Ground Coffee

Nescafe - Classic Instant, Taster's Choice Instant (Original)

O Organics - All Coffee Beans

Prestige - 100% Colombian Whole Bean

Publix - All Varieties

Safeway Brand - Decaf Classic Roast, Espresso Coffee Beans

Safeway Select - Whole Bean (Flavored)

Sanka - Decaf Coffee

C

Spartan Brand -
Coffee (French Roast, Instant, Instant Decaf, Regular)
Coffee Ground (Colombian, Decaf, Light, Regular)
Starbucks - All Coffee Beans, All Ground Coffee
Taster's Choice - Instant (Original)
Wegmans Brand -
Ground (100% Colombian, 100% Colombian Medium Roast,
Breakfast Blend Light Roast, Breakfast Blend Light Roast Decaf,
Caffeine Lite, Decaf, Espresso Dark Roast, French Roast,
Traditional)
Instant
Pure Origin Coffee (Day Break Roast, Ground Jamaican Mid Day,
Kona Evening, Smooth Morning, Sumatra Night)
Traditional Coffee Singles
Whole Bean Coffee (100% Colombian Medium Roast, Breakfast
Blend Light Roast, Espresso Dark Roast, Espresso Dark Roast
Decaf)
Winn Dixie - Colombian, Classic, Classic Decaf, Special Blend
Yuban -
Instant (Decaf, Reduced Caffeine/Lite, Regular)
Roast & Ground (Decaf, Reduced Caffeine/Lite, Regular)
Coffee Beans... see Coffee
Coffee Creamer... see Creamer
Coffee Syrup -
Nescafe - Ice Java Coffee Syrup (Cappuccino Fat Free, Chocolate
Mocha, French Vanilla Café Fat Free)
Cold Cuts... see Deli Meat
Cole Slaw Dressing... see Salad Dressing
Collards... see Greens
Communion Wafers
Ener-G▲ - Communion Wafers
Concentrate... see Drinks/Juice

cookies/cookie dough

C

Cones

    Let's Do...Organic - Gluten Free Ice Cream Cones

Cookie Mix... see also Cookies/Cookie Dough

    1-2-3 Gluten Free▲ - Chewy Chipless Scrumdelicious Cookies●, Lindsay's Lipsmackin' Roll Our & Cut Sugar Cookies●, Sweet Goodness Pan Bars●

    Cause You're Special▲ - Chocolate Chip, Classic Sugar

    Cherrybrook Kitchen - Gluten Free Sugar Cookie Mix *(Box Must Say Gluten-Free)*

    El Peto▲ - Old Fashion Sugar Cookie Mix

    Gifts Of Nature▲ - Triple Treat

    Gluten-Free Life▲ - The Ultimate Gluten Free Cookie Mix

    Gluten Free Sensations - Chocolate Chip Cookie Mix

    Hodgson Mill▲ - Gluten Free Cookie Mix

    Jules Gluten Free▲ - Graham Cracker/Gingersnap Mix●

    Maggie's Gluten Free Goodies▲ - Super Duper Sugar Cookie Mix

    Namaste Foods▲ - Blondies, Cookie

    Ruby Range - Old Fashioned Cookies Gluten Free Baking Mix●

    Simply Organic - Biscotti Mix●

    The Cravings Place▲ - Peanut Butter, Raisin Spice

    The Really Great Food Company▲ - Biscotti (Anise, Lemon Poppy), Butter, Chocolate Crinkle, Coconut Macaroon, Versatile

Cookies/Cookie Dough

    El Peto▲ - Almond Shortbread, Carob Chip, Chocolate (Chip, Coconut Macaroons), Cinnamon/Hazelnut, Coconut Macaroons, Gingersnaps, Hazelnut/Raspberry

    Ener-G▲ -

        Chocolate (Chip Biscotti, Chip Potato, Regular)

        Cinnamon

        Ginger

        Vanilla

C **Enjoy Life▲** - Chewy Chocolate Chip●, Double Chocolate Brownie●, Gingerbread Spice●, Happy Apple●, Lively Lemon●, No Oats "Oatmeal"●, Snickerdoodle●

French Meadow Bakery - Gluten Free (Chocolate Chip Cookie Dough●, Chocolate Chip Cookies●)

Glow Gluten Free ▲- Gingersnap, Snickerdoodle

Gluten Free Life▲ - Deluxe Sugar

Gluten-Free Creations▲ - Nutty Trail Mix●, Oatmeal Raisin●, Pecan Wedding●

Gluten-Free Essentials▲ - Vanilla Sugar Cookies

Gopal's - Nature's Gift Cookies (Almond Raisin, Goldenberry Brazil, Hazelnut Cherry, Macadamia Goji, Pineapple Flax)

Goraw - Super Cookies (Chocolate●, Original●)

Jennies - Zero Carb Macaroons (Carob, Coconut)

Jo-Sef▲ - Cinnamon, Lemon, Linzer, Orange, Sugar, Vanilla

Katz Gluten Free▲ - Cookies (Chocolate Dipped)

Kinnikinnick▲ -

Almond (Biscotti, Regular)

Ginger Snap

Lemon Cranberry

Kookie Karma - All Varieties●

Manischewitz - Macaroons (Chocolate Chip, Chocolate Chunk Cherry, Rocky Road)

Namaste Foods▲ - Blondies Mix, Cookie Mix

Nana's -

Cookie Bars (Berry Vanilla, Chocolate Munch, Nana Banana)

Cookie Bites (Ginger, Fudge, Lemon Dreams, Spice)

No Gluten Cookie (Chocolate, Chocolate Crunch, Ginger, Lemon)

Orgran▲ -

Amaretti Biscotti

Classic Chocolate Biscotti

Classic Chocolate Cookie

Itsy Bitsy Bears

Mini Outback Animals (Chocolate, Vanilla)

Outback Animals (Chocolate, Vanilla)

Wild Raspberry Fruit Flavored Biscuits

Pamela's Products▲ -

Extreme Chocolate Mini Cookies

Ginger (Mini Snapz, w/Sliced Almonds)

Organic Spicy Ginger w/Crystallized Ginger

Peanut Butter

Rose's Bakery▲ - Gingersnaps●, Macaroons●

Schar▲ - Ladyfingers, Shortbread Cookies

Cooking Spray

Publix - Grill

Winn Dixie - Grilling

Cooking Wine

Eden - Rice Mirin

Holland House - Marsala, Red, Sherry, Vermouth, White, White w/Lemon Flavor

Publix

Corn... *All Fresh Corn Is Gluten/Casein/Soy Free*

Albertsons - Canned (Creamed Style, Regular), Frozen

Birds Eye - All Plain Frozen Corn

C & W - All Plain Frozen Corn

Cascadian Farm - Organic Frozen (Super Sweet Corn, Sweet Corn)

Del Monte - All Plain Canned Corn

Food Club Brand - Canned (Cream Style, Golden, White, w/Peppers), Frozen (Golden, White)

Freshlike - All Frozen Plain Corn

Full Circle - Organic Frozen Whole Kernel Corn, Organic Gold Corn

Grand Selections - Frozen (Super Sweet Cut, White Shoepeg)

Great Value Brand (Wal-Mart) - Canned (Cream Style Corn, Golden Sweet Whole Kernel Corn, No Salt Added Golden Sweet Whole Kernel Corn)

C

Green Giant -
  Canned
    Cream Style Sweet Corn
    Mexicorn
    Niblets (Extra Sweet, No Salt Added, Whole Kernel Extra Sweet Corn, Whole Kernel Sweet Corn)
    Southwestern Style
    Super Sweet Yellow & White Corn
    White Shoepeg Corn
  Frozen
    Cream Style Corn
    Nibblers (12 Count, 24 Count)
    Steamers Niblets Corn
Haggen - Whole Kernel Corn
Hannaford Brand - Cream Style, Crisp & Sweet, Mexican Style, Whole Kernel
Health Market - Organic Whole Kernel
Home Harvest Brand - Canned, Frozen Whole Kernel Gold
Hy-Vee - Corn On The Cob, Cream Style (Golden Corn), Frozen Cut Golden Corn, Steam In A Bag Frozen Corn, Whole Kernel (Corn, Gold Corn, White Sweet Corn)
Kroger Brand - All Plain Corn (Canned, Frozen)
Laura Lynn - Corn (Cream Style, Gold 'N White, No Salt Whole Kernel, Vacuum Packed, Whole Kernel)
Lowes Foods Brand -
  Canned (White)
  Frozen (Corn Cob Full Ear, Corn Cob Mini Ear, Cut)
Meijer Brand -
  Canned (Cream Style, Golden Sweet Organic, Whole Kernel (Crisp & Sweet, Golden, Golden No Salt, White))
  Frozen (Corn Cob Mini Ear, Corn On Cob, Whole Kernel, Whole Kernel Golden)

C

Midwest Country Fare - Cream Style, Frozen Cut, Whole Kernel

Native Forest - Organic Cut Baby Corn

Nature's Promise - Organic Corn (Cut, On The Cob)

O Organics - Canned Whole Kernel, Frozen Golden Cut

Pictsweet - All Plain Frozen Corn

Publix -

> Canned (Cream Style Golden, Golden Sweet, Whole Kernel Crispy, Whole Kernel Crispy 50% Less Salt)

> Frozen (Corn On Cob, Cut)

Publix GreenWise Market - Organic Canned Whole Kernel

S&W - All Plain Canned Corn

Safeway Brand - Cream Style, Frozen Corn On The Cob, No Salt Whole Kernel, Steam In Bag (Petite, White)

Spartan Brand -

> Canned Corn

> Frozen (Baby Corn Blend, Corn On The Cob, Mini Ear Corn On The Cob, Plain, White Super Sweet)

Stop & Shop Brand - Corn (& Peas, Cut, Mexican Style, On The Cob, Super Sweet Corn On The Cob), Whole Kernel Corn

Trader Joe's - All Plain Frozen Corn

Wegmans Brand -

> Canned (Bread & Butter, Cream Style Golden Sweet, Crisp 'N Sweet Whole Kernel, Whole Kernel, Whole Kernel No Salt)

> Frozen (Baby Corn Cleaned And Cut, Bread & Butter Sweet Whole Kernel, Super Sweet Steamable)

Winn Dixie -

> Canned (Creamed Style, Mexican Style, White Whole Kernel, Yellow Whole Kernel, Yellow Whole Kernel No Salt)

> Frozen Corn (Organic Yellow Cut, Steamable Yellow Cut, White Cut, Yellow Cut)

> Frozen Corn On The Cob (Mini, Regular)

C   **Woodstock Farms** - Organic Frozen Cut Corn (Regular, Supersweet (Regular, White)), Toasted Corn

Corn Dog

    Ian's - Wheat Free Gluten Free Recipe Popcorn Turkey Corn Dogs

    S'Better Farms▲ - Beef Corn Dogs

Corn Oil... see Oil

Corn Starch... see Starch

Corn Syrup... see Syrup

Cornbread/Cornbread Mix

    Chi-Chi's - Fiesta Sweet Corn Cake Mix

    Bob's Red Mill▲ - Gluten Free Cornbread Mix

    Food-Tek Fast & Fresh - Dairy Free Minute Cornbread Mix

    Mixes From The Heartland▲ - Corn Bread Mix

    Orgran▲ - Cornbread & Muffin Mix

    The Really Great Food Company▲ - Cornbread Muffin Mix

Corned Beef... see also Beef

    Armour - Corned Beef Hash

    Dietz & Watson - Corned Beef Brisket, Corned Beef Flat (Extra Lean)

    Great Value Brand (Wal-Mart)

    Hormel - Corned Beef, Corned Beef Hash, Deli Sliced Cooked Corned Beef

    Meijer Brand - Hash

    Safeway Brand - Hash

    Wellshire Farms - Corned Beef Brisket (Regular, Whole), Round Corned Beef, Sliced Round Corned Beef

Cornflake Crumbs... see Coating

Cornish Hens... *All Fresh Poultry Is Gluten/Casein/Soy Free (Non-Marinated, Unseasoned)*

    Shelton's - Game Hens

Cornmeal

    Arrowhead Mills - Organic Blue, Organic Yellow

    El Peto▲ - Cornmeal

C

Hodgson Mill▲ -
  Organic Yellow
  Plain White
  Plain Yellow
Kinnikinnick▲
Safeway Brand - Yellow Corn Meal
Shiloh Farms - Corn Meal
Couscous
  Lundberg▲ - Brown Rice Couscous (Mediterranean Curry, Plain, Savory Herb)
Crabmeat... *All Fresh Seafood Is Gluten/Casein/Soy Free (Non-Marinated, Unseasoned)*
  Chicken Of The Sea - Jumbo Lump, Lump Crab, Original, White Crab
  Crown Prince - Natural (Fancy White Lump), Regular (Fancy Pink, Fancy White, Lump White)
  Great Value Brand (Wal-Mart) - Crab Meat
  Ocean Prince - Pink
Crackers
  Crunchmaster - Rice Crackers (Toasted Sesame●)
  Edward & Sons - Brown Rice Snaps (Onion Garlic, Salsa, Toasted Onion, Unsalted Plain, Unsalted Sesame, Vegetable)
  Ener-G▲ - Cinnamon, Seattle
  Kookie Karma - All Varieties●
  Orgran▲ - Crispbreads (Corn, Rice, Rice & Cracked Pepper, Rice & Garden Herb, Salsa Corn), Crispibites (Balsamic Herb, Corn, Onion & Chive), Crackers (Premium Deli)
  Real Foods - Corn Thins (Cracked Pepper & Lemon, Multigrain, Original, Sesame), Rice Thins (Wholegrain)
  Schar▲ - Table Crackers
Cranberries... *All Fresh Cranberries Are Gluten/Casein/Soy Free*
  Publix - Frozen Cranberries
  Oceanspray - Dried Cranberries (Original)

C Cranberry Sauce

Baxters

Great Value Brand (Wal-Mart)

Hannaford Brand - Jellied

Hy-Vee - Jellied, Whole Berry

Ocean Spray - Jellied, Whole Berry

S&W - Jellied, Whole Berry

Safeway Brand - Jellied, Whole Berry

Spartan Brand - Jellied, Whole Berry

Wegmans Brand - Jellied, Whole Berry

Wild Thymes - Cranberry Apple Walnut, Cranberry Fig, Cranberry Raspberry, Original

Winn Dixie - Jellied

Cream... see Milk Alternative and/or Creamer

Creamer

MimicCreme - Sugar Free Sweetened, Sweetened, Unsweetened

Crisps

Brothers All Natural▲ -

Fruit Crisps (Asian Pear, Banana, Fuji Apple, Pineapple, Strawberry, Strawberry Banana, White & Yellow Peach)

Potato Crisps (Black Pepper & Sea Salt, Fresh Onion & Garlic, Original w/Sea Salt, Szechuan Pepper & Fresh Chives)

Herr's - Veggie Crisps

Mr. Krispers -

Baked Rice Krisps (Barbecue●, Sea Salt & Pepper●)

Multi Seed Chips (Original●)

Orgran▲ - Crispibites (Balsamic Herb, Onion & Chive, Original Corn)

Croutons

Ener-G▲ - Plain Croutons

Cucumbers... *All Fresh Cucumbers Are Gluten/Casein/Soy Free*

Curry Paste

C

D

   A Taste Of Thai - Curry Paste (Green, Red, Yellow)

   Patak's - Curry Paste (Biryani, Madras, Tandoori, Tikka, Vindaloo)

   Sharwood's - Green, Red

   Thai Kitchen - Curry Paste (Green, Red)

Curry Powder

   Durkee

   McCormick

   Spice Island

   Tones

Custard

   Orgran▲ - Custard Mix

D

Deli Meat

   Applegate Farms -

      Natural (Black Forest Ham, Coppa, Genoa Salami, Herb Turkey, Honey & Maple Turkey Breast, Honey Ham, Hot Genoa Salami, Hot Soppressata, Pancetta, Pepperoni, Roast Beef, Roasted Turkey, Slow Cooked Ham, Smoked Turkey Breast, Soppressata, Turkey Bologna, Turkey Salami)

      Organic (Genoa Salami, Herb Turkey Breast, Roast Beef, Roasted Chicken, Smoked Chicken, Smoked Turkey Breast, Uncured Ham)

   Butterball -

      Extra Thin Turkey Breast (Honey Roasted, Oven Roasted, Smoked)

      Family Size (Honey Roasted Turkey Breast, Oven Roasted Turkey Breast, Smoked Turkey Breast, Turkey Bologna, Turkey Ham)

      Thick Sliced Turkey Breast (Honey Roasted, Oven Roasted, Smoked)

D

Thin Sliced Oven Roasted Chicken Breast

Thin Sliced Turkey Breast (Honey Roasted, Oven Roasted, Smoked)

Carl Buddig -

Deli Thin Sliced

Beef

Chicken

Ham

Honey Ham

Honey Turkey

Oven Roasted Turkey

Pastrami

Turkey

Extra Thin Sliced

Beef

Ham

Honey Ham

Honey Turkey

Turkey

Dietz & Watson -

Black Forest Knockwurst

Farmer John - Lunch Meats (Black Forest Ham, Bologna, Brown Sugar & Honey Ham, Cotto Salami, Headcheese, Premium Oven Roasted Turkey Breast)

Hannaford Brand -

Sliced (Cooked Ham, Danish Brand Ham, Honey Ham, Oven Roasted Turkey)

Thin Sliced (Black Forest Turkey, Honey Cured Turkey, Honey Ham, Oven Roasted Turkey, Roast Beef)

Hebrew National -

From The Deli Counter (Corned Beef, Pastrami)

Hillshire Farms -
  Deli Select
    Baked Ham
    Honey (Ham, Roasted Turkey Breast)
  Deli Select Premium Hearty Slices
    Honey (Ham, Roasted Turkey)
    Oven Roasted Turkey Breast
    Virginia Brand Baked Ham
  Deli Select Thin Sliced
    Brown Sugar Baked Ham
    Corned Beef
    Honey Roasted Turkey Breast
    Mesquite Smoked Turkey Breast
    Oven Roasted (Chicken Breast, Turkey Breast)
    Roast Beef
    Smoked (Chicken Breast, Ham, Turkey Breast)
  Deli Select Ultra Thin
    Brown Sugar Baked Ham
    Honey (Ham, Roasted Turkey Breast)
    Mesquite Smoked Turkey
    Oven Roasted Turkey Breast
    Pastrami
    Roast Beef
    Smoked Ham
Homeland - Hard Salami
Honeysuckle White -
  Chicken Breast Oil Browned
  Hickory Smoked Cooked Turkey Salami
  Hickory Smoked Turkey Ham

D

Hickory Smoked Turkey Pastrami
Lunch Meats Deli Sliced
  Hickory Smoked Honey Turkey Breast
  Hickory Smoked Turkey Breast
  Oven Roasted Turkey Breast
  Turkey Pastrami
Turkey Bologna
Turkey Breast Deli Meats
  Cajun Style Hickory Smoked
  Golden Roasted
  Hickory Smoked
  Hickory Smoked Peppered
  Honey Mesquite Smoked
  Oven Prepared
Turkey Breast Estate Recipe
  Buffalo Style
  Canadian Brand Maple
  Dry Roasted
  Hickory Smoked (Honey Pepper, Original)
  Honey Smoked
  Mesquite Smoked
Hormel -
Deli Sliced
  Black Forest Ham
  Cooked
    Corned Beef
    Ham
    Pastrami
  Honey Ham
  Oven Roasted Turkey Breast
  Prosciutto Ham

D

Diced Ham
Natural Choice
  Cooked Deli Ham
  Honey Deli (Ham, Turkey)
  Oven Roasted Deli Turkey
  Roast Beef
  Smoked Deli (Ham, Turkey)
  Uncured Hard Salami
Hy-Vee - Loaf (Old Fashioned, Spiced Luncheon)
Jennie-O -
Grand Champion Turkey Breast
  Hickory Smoked
  Honey Cured
  Mesquite Smoked
  Oven Roasted
Natural Choice Deli Counter Turkey Breast
  Applewood Smoked
  Honey Roasted
  Peppered
Premium Fresh Deli Counter Turkey Breast
  Golden Classic Herb Roasted
  Hickory Smoked Honey Roasted
  Honey Cured
  Mesquite Smoked
  Oven Roasted
Premium Seasoned Deli Counter Turkey Breast
  Bourbon Maple
  Cajun Style
  Cracked Pepper
  Sun Dried Tomato
  Sweet Maple

D

Norwestern Deli Turkey - Oven Roasted
Oscar Mayer -
Deli Fresh Meats
Cooked Ham (96% Fat Free, Regular)
Honey Ham
Oven Roasted (98% Fat Free Turkey, Chicken Breast, Turkey Breast)
Smoked (Ham, Turkey Breast)
Shaved Deli Fresh Meats
Black Forest Ham
Brown Sugar Ham
Cajun Seasoned Chicken Breast
Cracked Black Peppered Turkey Breast
French Dip Roast Beef
Honey Ham
Honey Smoked Turkey Breast
Oven Roasted Turkey Breast
Rotisserie Style Chicken Breast
Slow Roasted Roast Beef
Smoked Ham
Smoked Turkey Breast
Virginia Brand Ham
Thin Sliced Deli Fresh
97% Fat Free Smoked Ham
Brown Sugar Ham
Honey Smoked Turkey Breast
Oven Roasted Chicken Breast
Oven Roasted Turkey Breast
Smoked Turkey Breast
Primo Taglio -
Old Fashioned Maple Ham w/Natural Juices
Prosciutto Dry Cured Ham

D

    Roast Beef Coated w/Seasonings (Caramel Color Added)

    Salami Coated w/Gelatin & Black Pepper

Publix -

    Deli Pre Pack Sliced Lunch Meat

        Beef (Bologna, Bottom Round Roast)

        Cooked Ham

        Corned Beef

        Extra Thin Sliced (Honey Ham, Oven Roasted Turkey Breast, Smoked Turkey Breast)

        German Bologna

        Low Salt Ham

        Pickle & Pimento Loaf

        Smoked Turkey

        Spanish Style Pork

        Sweet Ham

        Tavern Ham

        Turkey Breast

        Virginia Brand Ham

Wegmans - Roast Beef Organic, Turkey Breast No Salt, Turkey Oven Browned

Winn Dixie - Thin Sliced (Cooked Ham, Honey Ham, Roast Beef, Oven Roasted Turkey, Smoked Honey Turkey, Smoked Turkey)

Dill Pickles... see Pickles

Dinner Meals... see Meals

Dip/Dip Mix

    Fantastic World Foods - Original Hummus

    Fritos - Bean, Hot Bean

    Road's End Organics - Non Dairy Nacho Chreese Dip (Mild, Spicy)

    Salpica - Chipotle Black Bean Dip

    Scarpetta - Spicy Red Pepper Spread

D **Sharwood's** - Green Label Mango Chutney & Chilli

UTZ - Mt. Misery Mike's Salsa Dip, Sweet Salsa Dip

Walden Farms - Fruit Dip (Caramel, Chocolate, Marshmallow), Veggie & Chip Dip (Bacon, Blue Cheese, French Onion, Ranch)

Donuts/Doughnuts

Ener-G▲ - Plain Doughnut (Holes, Regular)

Gluten-Free Creations▲ - Chocolate●, Cinnamon & Sugar●, Insane Chocolate●, Plain Jane●, Superb Sprinkles●

Kinnikinnick▲ - Chocolate Dipped, Cinnamon Sugar, Maple Dipped, Vanilla Glazed

Dressing... see Salad Dressing

Dried Fruit

Brothers All Natural▲ - Fruit Crisps (Asian Pear, Banana, Fuji Apple, Pineapple, Strawberry, Strawberry Banana, White & Yellow Peach)

Eden Organic - Cranberries, Montmorency Dried Tart Cherries, Wild Blueberries

Hy-Vee - Apples, Apricots, Banana Chips, Blueberries, Cherries, Cranberries, Mixed (Berries, Fruit), Pineapple

Member's Mark - 7 Fruit Blend, Mediterranean Dried Apricots

Nonuttin' Foods▲ - Fruit Snacks

Oceanspray - Dried Cranberries (Original)

Publix - Dried Plums

Safeway Brand - Berries & Cherries, Cranberries, Island Inspirations, Philippine Mango, Prunes, Raisins, Tropical Treasures

Spartan Brand - Cranberries

Sun-Maid -

Raisins

Baking

Golden

Natural California

Regular

Zante Currants

Traverse Bay Fruit Co. - Certified Organic Dried Tart Cherries, Dried Natural Cherries, Dried Tart Cherries

Wegmans Brand - Seedless Raisins

Woodstock Farms -

Apple Rings (Regular, Unsulphured)

Apricots Turkish

Banana Chips (Regular, Sweetened)

Black Mission Figs

Blueberries

Calmyrna Figs

Cherries Unsulphured

Cranberries Sweetened

Dates Deglet w/Pit

Flame Raisins

Ginger (Crystallized, Slices Unsulphured)

Goji Berries

Kiwi Slices

Mango (Diced, Slices (Regular, Unsulphured))

Medjool Dates w/Pit

Papaya Spears Lo Sugar Unsulphured

Pineapple Slices Unsulphured

Prunes Pitted

Thompson Raisins

Winn Dixie -

Apricots

Banana Chips

Blueberries

Cherries

Cranberries

Plums

Raisins (Golden, Organic, Regular)

D Drink Mix

Crystal Light -
Decaf Iced Tea (Lemon, Regular)
Fruit Punch
Green Tea Raspberry
Iced Tea (Peach, Raspberry, Regular)
Immunity Natural Cherry Pomegranate
Pineapple Orange
Raspberry (Lemonade, Peach)
Strawberry Kiwi
Sunrise (Berry Tangerine Morning, Classic Orange, Orange Wake Up, Ruby Red Grapefruit, Tangerine Strawberry, Tropical Morning)
White Grape

Flavor Aid -
Powdered Soft Drinks
Berry Punch
Cherry
Grape
Kiwi Watermelon
Lemon Lime
Lemonade
Orange
Raspberry
Strawberry
Tropical Punch

Hannaford Brand -
Regular (Cherry, Fruit Punch, Lemonade, Orange, Strawberry)
Sugar Free (Fruit Punch, Iced Tea, Lemon Lime, Lemonade, Raspberry Lemonade)

Hawaiian Punch - All Varieties

Hy-Vee -
>   Splash Drink Mix (Cherry, Grape, Lemonade, Orange, Strawberry, Tropical, Tropical Fruit Punch)
>
>   Sugar Free Splash Drink Mix (Fruit Punch, Iced Tea, Lemonade, Pink Lemonade, Raspberry)

Kool-Aid - Soft Drink Mix Sugar Sweetened (Cherry, Grape, Lemonade, Strawberry), Soft Drink Mix Unsweetened (Cherry, Grape, Lemonade, Strawberry, Tropical Punch)

Langers Juices - All Juices

Meijer Brand -
>   Breakfast Orange
>
>   Cherry
>
>   Chocolate Flavor
>
>   Grape
>
>   Ice Tea
>
>   Lemon Sugar Free
>
>   Lemonade
>
>   Lemonade Stix
>
>   Orange (Free & Lite, Regular)
>
>   Pink Lemonade (Regular, Sugar Free)
>
>   Punch
>
>   Raspberry Stix
>
>   Raspberry Sugar Free
>
>   Strawberry (Flavor, Regular)
>
>   Strawberry/Orange/Banana

Nestea - Iced Tea Mix Unsweetened (Decaf, Regular)

Safeway Brand - Cherry (Light, Regular), Peach (Light, Regular), Pink (Light, Regular), Spiced Apple Cider, Strawberry (Light, Regular), Sugar Free Raspberry & Lemonade

Snapple - All Diet Drink Mixes

Tang - Grape, Orange, Orange Kiwi, Tropical Passionfruit, Wild Berry

D   **Wegmans Brand** - Powdered Drink Mix (Lemonade Flavor, Pink Lemonade)

Winn Dixie -

> Regular (Cherry, Fruit Punch, Grape, Lemonade, Orange, Pink Lemonade, Raspberry, Strawberry Kiwi)

> Sugar Free (Fruit Punch, Lemon Iced Tea, Lemonade, Peach Iced Tea, Pink Lemonade)

Wyler's - All Powdered Soft Drinks (Light, Regular, Sugar Free)

Drinks/Juice (Non-Carbonated)... (Carbonated Drinks... see Soda Pop)

> **Apple & Eve** - All Vegetable & Fruit Juices *(Except Tribal Tonic Peach Mango Energy Green Tea)*

> **Campbell's** - Tomato Juice (Low Sodium, Organic, Original)

> **Capri Sun** -

>> Coastal Cooler Strawberry Banana Blend

>> Grape

>> Mountain Cooler

>> Orange

>> Pacific Cooler Mixed Fruit

>> Splash Cooler Mixed Fruit

>> Strawberry

>> Strawberry Raspberry Blend

>> Sunrise Berry Strawberry Tangerine

>> Sunrise Orange Wake Up

>> Sunrise Tropical Morning

>> Surfer Cooler Mixed Fruit Blend

>> Tropical Punch

>> Wild Cherry Blend

> **Cascadian Farms** - Organic Frozen Juice Concentrate (Apple, Cranberry, Grape, Lemonade, Orange, Raspberry)

> **Ceres** - All Varieties

> **Country Time** - Lemonade

D

Dei Fratelli - Juice (Tomato (Regular, Tasty Tom Spicy), Vegetable)

Dole - All Fruit Juice

Eden Organic - Apple Juice, Cherry Concentrate, Montmorency Tart Cherry Juice

Enviga - Sparkling Green Tea (Berry, Regular)

Food Club Brand -

Cranberry (Apple, Grape, Light Grape, Light Raspberry, Raspberry, White Cranberry Strawberry)

Frozen (Apple, Lemonade, OJ Original, OJ Pulp Free, Pink Lemonade)

Juices (Apple, Cranberry, Grapefruit & Tangerine, Lemon, Lime, Pineapple, Pomegranate, Pomegranate Blueberry, Prune, Ruby Red Grapefruit, Tomato, Vegetable, White Grape, White Grapefruit)

Refrigerated (OJ Groves Best, OJ Premium, OJ (w/Calcium, w/Omega 3))

Fruit2O - All Varieties

Full Circle - Organic (Apple Natural, Blueberry 100% Juice, Cranberry Cocktail, Cranberry Raspberry, Grape 100% Juice, Orange Carafe, Tomato Juice, Vegetable Juice)

Fuze - All Varieties *(Except 'Refresh' Drinks)*

Gardner Groves - 100% Grapefruit Juice

Gold Peak - Iced Tea (Diet, Green Sweetened, Lemon, Sweetened, Unsweetened)

Great Value Brand (Wal-Mart) -

From Concentrate

100% Juice Apple Juice Punch Blend

100% Juice Unsweetened Apple Juice

Fruit Punch

Natural Strength Lemon Juice

Tomato Juice

Vegetable Juice

D

Frozen Juice Concentrate
  Country Style Orange Juice Pure Unsweetened
  Florida Grapefruit Juice Pure Unsweetened
  Fruit Punch
  Grape Juice Drink
  Limeade
  Orange Juice w/Calcium
  Pink Lemonade
Juice
  100% Juice Apple Juice (Juice Boxes)
  100% Juice Fruit Punch (Juice Boxes)
  Prune Juice
Refrigerated Drinks
  Country Style Orange Juice
  Fruit Punch
  Grape Drink
  Orange Juice (Regular, w/Calcium)

Hannaford Brand -
  From Concentrate (Apple, Apple & Grape Blend, Berry Blend, Blueberry Cranberry, Cherry Blend, Cranberry Juice Cocktail, Fruit Punch, Grape Blend, Grapefruit, Light Cranberry, Light Grape Cranberry, Light Raspberry Cranberry, Low Sodium Vegetable Juice, Orange Juice, Raspberry Cranberry, Ruby Red Grapefruit, Tomato Juice, Vegetable Juice, White Cranberry Peach)
  Premium Juice Blend (Cranberry Flavored, Cranberry Raspberry, Grape Cranberry)

Hansen's - All (Bottled Juices, Diet Green Tea Sodas, Diet Soda, Junior Juices, Juice Slams, Natural Green Tea Sodas, Natural Soda, Natural Soda Mixers, Organic Juice Slams, Organic Junior Water, Smoothies, Sparking Green Tea Sleek, Sparkling Sleek)

Hawaiian Punch - Light, Original

Home Harvest Brand - Apple Juice, Cranberry Juice Cocktail, Original Orange Juice, Tomato Juice, Vegetable Juice Cocktail

Honest Ade - Cranberry Lemonade, Limeade, Orange Mango w/Mangosteen, Pomegranate Blue, Super Fruitpunch

Honest Kids - Berry Berry Good Lemonade, Goodness Greatness, Tropical Tangopunch

Honest Mate -

Agave Mate

Sublime Mate

Tropical Mate

Hood - All Juices

Hy-Vee -

100% Juice Blend (Cranberry, Cranberry Apple, Cranberry Raspberry)

Concord Grape Juice

Frozen Concentrate (Apple (Light, Regular), Fruit Punch, Grape Juice Cocktail, Grapefruit Juice, Lemonade, Limeade, Orange (Regular, w/Calcium), Pineapple, Pink Lemonade)

Juice Cocktail From Concentrate (Cranberry, Cranberry Apple, Cranberry Grape, Cranberry Raspberry, Grapefruit, Lemon, Light Cranberry Raspberry, Ruby Red Grapefruit)

Juice From Concentrate (100% Apple, 100% Unsweetened Prune, 100% White Grape, Apple, Apple Kiwi, Country Style Orange, Lemonade, Light Apple Raspberry, Light Grape Cranberry, Orange Juice, Orange Juice w/Calcium, Pineapple, Pomegranate, Prune Juice, Tomato, Unsweetened Apple Cider, Vegetable)

Izze -

Sparkling Juice Beverages

Blackberry

Blueberry

Clementine

Grapefruit

Peach

Pomegranate

D **Lakewood** - All Juices (Organic)
Lowes Foods Brand -
    Juice
        Apple (Natural, Regular)
        Concord Grape
        Cranberry Apple
        Cranberry Cocktail (Light, Regular)
        Cranberry Grape (Light, Regular)
        Cranberry Raspberry
        Grape Cocktail Light
        Lemon (Regular, Squeeze)
        Orange (Regular, Unsweetened)
        Pink Grapefruit
        Premium Cranberry Cocktail 100% Juice
        Prune
        Ruby Red Grapefruit Tangerine
        Tomato
        Vegetable Cocktail
        White (Grape, Grapefruit)
Lucky Leaf - Apple (Cider, Juice, Premium Juice)
Manischewitz - Grape Juice
Marsh Brand - Orange Juice (Refrigerated)
Meijer Brand -
    100% Juice (Berry, Cherry, Cranberry/Raspberry, Grape, Punch)
    Cranberry Juice Drink (Grape, Raspberry, Strawberry, White)
    Drink Thirst Quencher (Fruit Punch, Lemon Lime, Orange)
    Frozen Concentrate Juice (Apple, Fruit Punch, Grape, Grapefruit, Lemonade, Limeade, Orange, Pink Lemonade, White Grape)
    Frozen Concentrate Orange Juice (High Pulp, Pulp Free, w/Calcium)

D

Fruit Punch (Genuine, Light, Regular)

Juice (Apple, Apple Natural, Cherry, Grape, Grapefruit, Fruit Mix, Lemon, Lime, Pineapple, Pink Grapefruit, Prune, Ruby Red Grapefruit, Tangerine & Ruby Red, White Grape, White Grapefruit)

Juice Blend (Acai & Blueberry, Acai & Grape, Pomegranate & Blueberry, Pomegranate & Cranberry, White Cranberry, White Grape & Peach, White Grape & Raspberry)

Juice Cocktail (Cranapple, Cranberry (Light, Regular), Cranberry Grape (Light, Regular), Cranberry Raspberry (Light, Regular), Cranberry Strawberry, Cranberry White Peach, Light Grape Splenda, Ruby Red Grapefruit (Light, Light 22%, Regular), White Cranberry, White Cranberry Peach, White Cranberry Strawberry, White Grape, White Grapefruit)

Juice Refrigerated Orange (Original, Reconstituted)

Juice Refrigerated Orange Premium (Calcium Carafe, Carafe, Hi Pulp Carafe, Original, Pulp, w/Calcium)

Lemon Juice Squeeze Bottle

Orange Reconstituted (Original, Pulp, w/Calcium)

Organic Juice (Apple, Concord Grape, Cranberry, Lemonade)

Splash (Berry Blend, Strawberry Kiwi, Tropical Blend)

Midwest Country Fare - 100 % Unsweetened From Concentrate (Apple Cider, Apple Juice), Cranberry, Cranberry Apple, Cranberry Raspberry, Grape

Minute Maid -

Lemonade (Light, Original, Pink)

Limonada/Limeade

Orange Juice (Country Style, Heart Wise, Home Squeezed Style, Kids +, Low Acid, Original, Original + Calcium, Pulp Free)

Orange Tangerine

Punch (Berry, Citrus, Fruit, Grape, Tropical)

Mondo - All Fruit Squeezers

Mott's - All Varieties

D

Musselman's - Apple (Cider, Fresh Pressed Apple Cider, Juice, Premium Juice, Sparkling Cider)

Nantucket Nectars - All Varieties

Nestea - Citrus Green Tea (Diet, Regular), Lemon (Diet, Sweetened), Red Tea, White Tea Berry Honey (Diet, Regular)

Nestle - Juicy Juice (All Flavors), Juicy Juice Harvest Surprise (All Flavors)

Newman's Own -

Grape Juice

Green Tea w/Honey

Lemon Aided Iced Tea

Lemonade (Lightly Sweetened, Old Fashioned, Organic, Pink)

Limeade

Orange Mango

Organic Virgin Lemonade

Razz Ma Tazz Raspberry

O Organics - Bottled Juices (Apple, Berry Blend, Blueberry Blend, Cranberry Cocktail, Grape, Lemonade, Unfiltered Apple), Orange Juice (Refrigerated)

Ocean Spray - All Varieties

Odwalla -

All Natural Carrot Juice

All Natural Lemonade

All Natural Orange Juice

All Natural Smoothie (Mango Tango, Strawberry Banana)

B Monster (Blueberry B)

C Monster (Citrus C, Strawberry C)

Mo' Beta

Mojito Mambo

Pomegranate Strawberry

Serious Energy (Tropical Energy)

Serious Focus (Apple Raspberry)

Wholly Grain (Tropical Medley)

Organic Valley - Orange Juice (Pulp Added, Pulp Free, w/Calcium) **D**
Powerade - Grape, Ion 4 Mountain Berry Blast
Publix -
From Concentrate
Orange Juice (Regular, w/Calcium)
Ruby Red Grapefruit Juice
Refrigerated
Premium Orange Juice (Calcium Plus, Grove Pure, Old Fashioned, Original)
Premium Ruby Red Grapefruit Juice
Shelf Stable
Apple
Cranberry (Apple Juice Cocktail, Juice Cocktail, Reduced Calorie Cocktail, w/Calcium)
Grape
Grape Cranberry Juice Cocktail
Lemonade (Deli Old Fashion)
Pineapple
Raspberry Cranberry Juice Cocktail
Ruby Red Grapefruit (Regular, w/Tangerine)
Tomato
White Grape
Publix GreenWise Market - Organic (Apple, Cranberry, Grape, Lemonade, Tomato)
R. W. Knudsen -
Juice
Black Cherry
Black Currant
Blueberry
Blueberry Pomegranate
Cranberry
Cranberry Pomegranate

D

Lemon Ginger Echinacea
Morning Blend
Organic Acai Berry
Organic Cranberry Blueberry
Organic Pomegranate
Organic Prune
Organic Tomato
Pomegranate

ReaLemon - 100% Lemon Juice
ReaLime - 100% Lime Juice
Safeway Brand -

Frozen (Apple, Berry Punch, Cranberry, Grape, Lemonade,
Limeade, Orange, Orange Country Style, Orange w/Calcium,
Pink Lemonade, Raspberry Lemonade)

Juice

Apple (Cider, Regular)
Cranberry (Apple, Cocktail, Light Cocktail, Light Raspberry,
Raspberry)
Grape (Light, Regular)
Grapefruit (Cocktail, Pink, Regular, Ruby Red Cocktail, White)
Lemon
Orange
Prune
Tomato
Vegetable
White Grape

Shelby's Grove - Apple Juice 100% Juice
Simply Apple
Simply Grapefruit
Simply Lemonade - Original, w/Raspberry
Simply Limeade

D

Simply Orange - Calcium Pulp Free, Country Stand Medium Pulp w/Calcium, High Pulp, Pulp Free, w/Pineapple, w/Mango

Snapple - All (100% Juices, Diet Drinks, Juice Drinks, Teas, Flavored Waters) *(Except Go Bananas, Lemonade, Snapple Apple, Pink Lemonade)*

SoBe -

　Elixir (Orange Carrot)

　Energy (Berry, Citrus, Tropical)

　Green Tea

　Lean Diet (Mango Melon)

　Nirvana (Mango Melon)

　Power (Fruit Punch)

Sonoma Sparkler - Natural (Peach, Pear, Raspberry), Organic (Apple, Lemonade)

Spartan Brand -

　Apple Juice (Natural, Regular)

　Cranberry Juice Cocktail (Low Calorie, Regular)

　Cranberry Juice Drink (Apple, Grape, Raspberry, Strawberry)

　Frozen Concentrate (Apple Juice, Grape Juice Cocktail, Fruit Punch, Grapefruit Juice, Lemonade, Orange Juice (Country Style, Pulp Free, Regular, w/Calcium), Pink Lemonade)

　Grape Juice (Regular, White)

　Grapefruit Juice

　Lemon Juice

　Premium Orange Juice (Country Style Pulp, Regular, w/Calcium)

　Premium Ruby Red Grapefruit

　Prune Juice

　Reconstituted Orange Juice (Country Style Pulp, Regular, w/Calcium)

　Ruby Red Grapefruit Juice

　Tomato Juice

　Vegetable Juice Cocktail

D **SunnyD** - All Varieties

Tipton Grove - Apple Juice 100% Juice

Trader Joe's - Organic Mango Lemonade

Tropicana - All 100% Juices

V8 -

Diet Splash (Berry Blend, Tropical Blend)

Splash (Berry Blend, Fruit Medley, Mango Peach, Strawberry Kiwi Blend, Tropical Blend)

V-Fusion (Acai Berry, Goji Raspberry, Passionfruit Tangerine, Peach Mango, Pomegranate Blueberry, Strawberry Banana, Tropical Orange)

V-Fusion Light (Peach Mango, Pomegranate Blueberry, Strawberry Banana)

Vegetable Juice (Calcium Enriched, Fiber, Low Sodium, Organic, Original, Spicy Hot)

Vruit - Apple Carrot, Berry Veggie, Orange Veggie, Tropical

Wegmans Brand -

100% Juice

Cranberry (Blend, Raspberry)

Ruby Red Grapefruit Blend

Frozen Juice Concentrate

Apple

Fruit Punch

Lemonade

Limeade

Pink Lemonade

Juice

Apple

Apple Natural

Cranberry (Peach, Raspberry, Regular)

Grape (Juice Cocktail, Regular, White)

Grapefruit

D

Juice Blends (Berry, Cherry, Concord Grape Cranberry, Cranberry Apple, Orange Peach Mango, Ruby Red Grapefruit, Sparkling Cranberry, White Grape Cranberry, White Grape Peach)

Lemon Juice Reconstituted

Orange (Regular, Unsweetened)

Prune

White Grape (Peach Blend, Raspberry Blend, Regular)

Juice From Concentrate

100% Juice (Orange, Tomato, Vegetable (No Salt Added, Regular))

Blueberry Flavor Juice Blend

Lemon

Lemonade

Limeade

Orange Juice (Calcium Enriched, Regular, w/Calcium)

Pomegranate Flavor Juice Blend

Prune

Organic Juice From Concentrate

Apple

Apricot Nectar

Cranberry

Mango Nectar

Orange

Punch (Berry, Fruit, Pineapple Orange)

Premium 100% Juice

Orange (Extra Pulp, No Pulp, Some Pulp, w/Calcium, w/Calcium & Vitamins)

Ruby Red Grapefruit

Premium Orange Juice (No Pulp, Some Pulp)

D

Sparkling Beverage

    Calorie Free (Lemon, Mandarin Orange, Mixed Berry, Tangerine Lime, Raspberry)

    Diet (Black Cherry, Cranberry Raspberry, Key Lime, Kiwi Strawberry, Mixed Berry, Peach, Peach Grapefruit, Tangerine Lime, White Grape)

    Lime, Grape Juice Alcohol Free, Lemonade

    Sparkling Grape Juice Alcohol Free (Pink, Red, White)

Welch's - All Varieties

Winn & Lovett - Juice (Black Cherry, Cranberry, Pomegranate)

Winn Dixie -

    Juice (Cranberry, Cranberry Apple, Cranberry Raspberry, Premium Apple, Light Cranberry, Light Cranberry Grape, Light Grape, Pomegranate Blend, Pomegranate Blueberry Blend, Pomegranate Cranberry Blend, Reconstituted Lemon, Ruby Red Grapefruit, Ruby Red Grapefruit Cocktail, Vegetable)

    Juice From Concentrate (Apple Cider, Apple, Grape, Grapefruit, Orange, Orange w/Calcium, Pink Lemonade, Prune, Prune w/Pulp, White Grape)

    Nectar Drinks (Guava, Mango, Mango Pineapple Guava, Peach, Pear)

    Organic Juice (Apple, Cranberry, Grape, Lemonade, Mango Acai Berry Blend, Orange Mango Blend, Tomato)

    Orange Juice (From Concentrate, From Concentrate w/Calcium, Premium Not From Concentrate)

Woodstock Farms - Non Organic Juices (All Varieties), Organic Juices (All Varieties)

Duck... *All Fresh Poultry Is **Gluten/Casein/Soy Free (Non-Marinated, Unseasoned)***

Shelton's - Duckling

Wellshire Farms - Smoked Duck Breast

Dumplings

Mixes From The Heartland▲ - Country Dumpling Mix●

E

Egg Replacer/Substitute
  Albertsons - Egg Substitute (Amazing Eggs, Egg Whites)
  All Whites - All Varieties
  Better'n Eggs - All Varieties
  Eggbeaters - Garden Vegetable, Original, Southwestern Style
  Ener-G▲ - Egg Replacer
  Hy-Vee - Refrigerated Egg Substitute
  Lucerne - Best Of The Egg
  Meijer Brand - Refrigerated Egg Substitute
  Orgran▲ - No Egg Egg Replacer
  Publix - Egg Stirs
  Spartan Brand - Eggmates
  Wegmans Brand - Egg Busters, Liquid Egg Whites
Eggplant... *All Fresh Eggplant Is Gluten/Casein/Soy Free*
  Tasty Bite - Punjab Eggplant
Eggs... *All Fresh Eggs Are Gluten/Casein/Soy Free*
Enchilada Sauce
  Frontera - Chipotle Garlic, Classic Red Chile
  Las Palmas - Red
  Safeway Select - Mild
Energy Bars... see Bars
Energy Drinks
  AMP - Lightning, Sugar Free, w/Green Tea
  Hansen's - All Varieties
  Inko's - White Tea Energy
  NOS - Energy Drink
  Red Bull - Cola, Energy Shots, Regular, Sugar Free
  Red Rain - Diet, Regular
  Rehab

E English Muffins

    Ener-G▲ - Brown Rice English Muffins w/Flax, English Muffins

F   **Foods By George**▲ - English Muffins (Cinnamon Currant, No Rye Rye, Plain)

    Kinnikinnick▲ - Tapioca Rice

Espresso... see Coffee

Extract

    Albertsons - Imitation Vanilla, Pure Vanilla

    Durkee - Vanilla (Imitation, Pure)

    Flavorganics - Almond, Anise, Chocolate, Coconut, Hazelnut, Lemon, Orange, Peppermint, Rum, Vanilla

    Hannaford Brand - Imitation (Almond, Vanilla), Pure (Lemon, Vanilla)

    Hy-Vee - Pure Vanilla

    Marcin - Pure Vanilla

    Marcum - Pure Vanilla

    McCormick - Pure Lemon, Pure Vanilla

    Meijer Brand - Imitation Vanilla, Vanilla

    Nielsen-Massey - Madagascar Bourbon Pure Vanilla●

    Publix - Almond, Lemon, Vanilla

    Spartan Brand - Imitation Vanilla, Vanilla

    Spice Island - Vanilla (Imitation, Pure)

    Tones - Vanilla (Imitation, Pure)

    Wegmans Brand - Vanilla Extract

F

Fajita Seasoning Mix... see also Seasonings

    McCormick - Seasoning Packet

    Safeway Brand

Falafel Mix

    Authentic Foods▲

    Orgran▲

Fettuccini... see Pasta

Fiber

    Kinnikinnick▲ - Easy White Fiber Mix, Pea Hull Fibre

Fish... *All Fresh Fish Is Gluten/Casein/Soy Free (Non-Marinated, Unseasoned)*

    Chicken Of The Sea -

        Canned (Jack Mackerel, Pink Salmon Chunk Style In Water, Pink Salmon Traditional Style)

        Pouch (Smoked Pacific Salmon)

    Crown Prince -

        Crosspacked Brisling Sardines In Olive Oil

        Jack Mackerel In Water

        One Layer Brisling Sardines In Mustard

        Sardines In (Hot Tomato Sauce, Tomato Sauce, Water)

        Skinless & Boneless In Olive Oil

        Two Layer Brisling Sardines In Olive Oil

    Crown Prince Natural -

        Alaskan Pink Salmon

        One Layer Brisling Sardines In (Mustard, Spring Water)

        Skinless & Boneless Pacific Pink Salmon

        Skinless & Boneless Sardines In (Olive Oil, Water)

        Smoked Alaskan Coho Salmon

        Two Layer Brisling Sardines In Olive Oil

    Dr. Praeger's - All Natural Potato Crusted Gluten Free (Fish Fillets, Fish Sticks, Fishies)

    Full Circle -

        All Natural Fillets (Alaskan Cod, Alaskan Sockeye Salmon, Skinless Mahi Mahi)

        All Natural Steaks (Alaskan Halibut, Swordfish, Yellowfin Tuna)

    Hy-Vee - Canned Alaskan Pink Salmon, Frozen (Salmon, Tilapia), Red Salmon

    Ian's - Wheat Free Gluten Free Recipe (Fish Sticks, Lightly Battered Fish)

F

Meijer Brand - Canned Salmon (Pink, Sock Eye Red)

Morey's - Wild Alaskan Salmon

Publix - Fillets (Bass, Cod, Flounder, Haddock, Halibut, Mahi Mahi, Orange Roughy, Snapper, Swordfish, Whiting)

Wegmans Brand -

Alaskan Halibut

Atlantic Salmon Fillets (Farm Raised)

Chilean Sea Bass

Lobster Tail

Orange Roughy

Pacific Cod

Smoked Salmon (Nova, Scottish Style)

Sockeye Salmon

Swordfish

Tilapia Fillets (Farm Raised)

Yellowfin Tuna (Sashimi Grade)

Winn Dixie - Frozen (Grouper, Tilapia)

Fish Sauce

A Taste Of Thai - Regular

Thai Kitchen - Regular

Fish Sticks

Dr. Praeger's - All Natural Potato Crusted Gluten Free (Fish Sticks, Fishies)

Ian's - Wheat Free Gluten Free Recipe Fish Sticks

Flax Seed

Arrowhead Mills - Flax Seed Meal, Flax Seeds (Golden, Regular)

Bob's Red Mill▲ - Flaxseed Meal (Golden, Original), Organic Flaxseed (Golden, Original)

El Peto▲ - Whole

Hodgson Mill▲ - Organic Golden Milled, Travel Flax All Natural Milled, Travel Flax Organic Golden Milled

Nature's Path - Organic FlaxPlus (Meal, Flaxseeds)

Spectrum - Organic Ground Essential Flax Seed

Flax Seed Oil... see Oil

Flour

Amazing Grains - Montina (All Purpose Flour Blend●, Pure Baking Supplement●)

Andrea's Fine Foods▲ - Gluten Free Flour Blend, Super Fine Grind Rice (Brown, Sweet)

Arrowhead Mills - All Purpose Baking Mix, Brown Rice, Organic (Buckwheat, Millet, White Rice)

Authentic Foods▲ -

Almond Meal

Arrowroot

Bette's Four Flour Blend

Brown Rice Flour Superfine

Garbanzo

Garfava

Gluten Free Classical Blend

Multi Blend Gluten Free

Potato (Flour, Starch)

Sorghum

Sweet Rice Flour Superfine

Tapioca

White (Corn, Rice Flour Superfine)

Bob's Red Mill▲ -

Almond Meal/Flour

Black Bean

Brown Rice

Fava Bean

Garbanzo Bean

Garbanzo & Fava

F

Gluten Free (All Purpose Baking, Sweet White Sorghum)

Green Pea

Hazelnut Meal/Flour

Millet

Organic (Amaranth, Brown Rice, Coconut, Quinoa, White Rice)

Potato

Sweet White Rice

Tapioca

Teff

White (Bean, Rice)

Chateau Cream Hill Estates - Lara's Whole Grain Oat Flour●

ConAgra Mills -

5 Grain Whole Grain Blend●

Conventional (Amaranth Seed●, Millet Seed●, Quinoa Seed●, Sorghum Seed●, Teff Seed●, Whole Amaranth Flour●, Whole Millet Flour●, Whole Quinoa Flour●, Whole Sorghum Flour●, Whole Teff Flour●)

Organic (Amaranth Seed●, Millet Seed●, Quinoa Seed●, Whole Amaranth Flour●, Whole Millet Flour●, Whole Quinoa Flour●)

Deerfields Bakery▲ - Quick Mix For Sugar Buttons

Domata - Gluten Free All Purpose Flour●

Dowd & Rogers▲ - California Almond, Italian Chestnut

El Peto▲ - All Purpose Flour Mix, Arrowroot, Bean, Brown Rice, Corn, Flax Seed, Garbanzo Fava Bean, Millet, Organic Amaranth, Potato, Quinoa, Sorghum, Sweet Rice, Tapioca Starch, White Rice

Ener-G▲ -

Brown Rice

Gluten Free Gourmet Blend

Potato (Flour, Starch)

Sweet Rice

Tapioca

White Rice

flour

F

Expandex▲ - Modified Tapioca Starch●

Flour Nut - Almond Flour

Gifts Of Nature▲ - All Purpose●, Baby Lima Bean, Brown Rice, Tapioca, Sweet Rice, White Rice

Gillian's Foods▲ -
Brown Rice
Chick Pea
Imported Tapioca
Potato (Regular, Starch)
Rice

Glutano▲ - Flour Mix It!

Gluten-Free Creations▲ - Baking Flours (Basic, Enriched, Sweet)

Hodgson Mill▲ - Brown Rice, Buckwheat

Jules Gluten Free▲ - All Purpose Flour●

Kinnikinnick▲ -
All Purpose Celiac
Brown Rice
Corn
Sweet Rice
White Rice

Laurel's Sweet Treats▲ - Baking Flour Mix

Lotus Foods - Bhutanese Red Rice Flour

Lundberg▲ - Brown Rice Flour (California Nutra Farmed, Organic California)

Montana Monster Munchies - Whole Grain Oat Flour●

Montina - All Purpose Baking Flour Blend, Pure Baking Supplement

Namaste Foods▲ - Perfect Flour Blend

Nu-World Foods - Amaranth (Flour●, Puffed●, Toasted Bran Flour●)

Only Oats - Oat Flour●

Orgran▲ - All Purpose Pastry Mix, Gluten Substitute, Plain All Purpose, Self Raising

F

    Pocono - Buckwheat

    Ruby Range - Mesquite

    Shiloh Farms - Almond, Brown Rice, Corn, Mesquite, Potato, Quinoa, Tapioca, Teff

Food Coloring

    Durkee - Blue, Caramel, Egg Shade, Green, Red, Yellow

    Hy-Vee - Assorted

    McCormick - All Varieties

    Spice Islands - Blue, Caramel, Egg Shade, Green, Red, Yellow

    Tones- Blue, Caramel, Egg Shade, Green, Red, Yellow

Frankfurters... see Sausage

French Fries...see also Potatoes

    Alexia Foods -

        Crispy Potatoes w/Seasoned Salt Waffle Fries

        Julienne Fries Spicy Sweet Potato

        Julienne Fries Sweet Potato

        Julienne Fries w/Sea Salt Yukon Gold

        Olive Oil & Sea Salt Oven Fries

        Olive Oil Rosemary & Garlic Oven Fries

        Olive Oil Sun Dried Tomatoes & Pesto Oven Reds

        Organic (Classic Oven Crinkles, Oven Crinkles Onion & Garlic, Oven Crinkles Salt & Pepper, Yukon Gold Julienne Fries w/Sea Salt)

        Yukon Gold Potatoes w/Seasoned Salt Potato Nuggets

    Cascadian Farm - Organic Frozen (Country Style Potatoes, Crinkle Cut French Fries, Shoe String Fries, Spud Puppies, Straight Cut French Fries, Wedge Cut Oven Fries)

    Funster - Natural Potato Letters

    Ian's - Alphatots

    Meijer Brand - Quickie Crinkles

    Publix - Frozen Southern Style Hash Browns

Woodstock Farms - Organic Frozen (Crinkle Cut Oven Fries, Shredded Hash Browns, Tastee Taters)

French Toast

Ian's - Wheat Free Gluten Free Recipe French Toast Sticks

Frosting... see Baking Decorations & Frostings

Frozen Desserts... see Ice Cream

Frozen Dinners... see Meals

Frozen Vegetables... see Mixed Vegetables

Frozen Yogurt... see Ice Cream

Fruit Bars... see Bars

Fruit Cocktail

Albertsons - Heavy Syrup, Light

Del Monte -
Canned/Jarred Fruit (All Varieties)
Fruit Snack Cups (Metal, Plastic)

Food Club Brand - In Heavy Syrup, Lite

Great Value Brand (Wal-Mart) -
Fruit Cocktail In Heavy Syrup
Fruit Cocktail Sweetened With Splenda

Hannaford Brand - Extra Light Syrup, Heavy Syrup, No Sugar Added

Hy-Vee - Lite, Regular

Meijer Brand - Heavy Syrup, In Juice, In Pear Juice Lite

Midwest Country Fare

Laura Lynn - Canned

Lowes Foods Brand - In Heavy Syrup, In Juice

Publix - Canned (In Heavy Syrup, Lite In Pear Syrup)

Safeway Brand - Canned (Lite, Regular)

Spartan Brand - Heavy Syrup, Light Juice

Stop & Shop Brand - Heavy Syrup, Pear Juice

Wegmans Brand - In Heavy Syrup, In Pear Juice

Winn Dixie - Fruit Cocktail (Heavy Syrup, Light Syrup)

F Fruit Drinks... see Drinks/Juice

Fruit Leather...see also Fruit Snacks

   Stretch Island Fruit Co. - All Varieties

Fruit Salad

   Meijer Brand - Tropical

   Native Forest - Organic Tropical

   Safeway Brand - Tropical Fruit

Fruit Snacks

   Annie's▲ - Organic Bunny Fruit Snacks (Berry Patch, Sunny Citrus, Summer Strawberry, Tropical Treat)

   Brothers All Natural▲ - Fruit Crisps (Asian Pear, Banana, Fuji Apple, Pineapple, Strawberry, Strawberry Banana, White & Yellow Peach)

   Fruit By The Foot -

      Berry Berry Twist

      Berry Tie Dye

      Color By The Foot

      Flavor Kickers (Berry Blast, Tropical Twist)

      Mini Feet (Berry Wave)

      Razzle Blue Blitz

      Strawberry

      Variety Pack (Berry Tie Dye, Color By The Foot, Strawberry)

      Watermelon

   Fruit Flavored Snacks -

      Barbie

      Fairies Tinkerbell

      High School Musical

      John Deere

      Mickey Mouse Clubhouse

      Nickelodeon Sponge Bob Square Pants

      Operation

      Pixar Finding Nemo

      Pixar Toy Story

F

Power Rangers Super Legends

Princess

Strawberry Shortcake

Fruit Gushers -

Punch Berry

Rockin' Blue Raspberry

Strawberry Splash

Triple Berry Shock

Tropical Flavors

Watermelon Blast

Fruit Roll-Ups -

Berry Berry Cool

Blastin' Berry Hot Colors

Crazy Pix (Cool Chix Berry Wave, Wild Ones Blastin' Berry)

Electric Blue Raspberry

Flavor Wave

Stickerz (Berry Cool Punch, Stars Mixed Berry, Twisters Tropical Berry)

Strawberry (Kiwi Kick, Regular)

Tropical Tie Dye

Variety Pack (Cherry Orange Wildfire, Strawberry, Tropical Tie Dye)

Great Value Brand (Wal-Mart) - Fruit Smiles

Welch's -

Berries N' Cherries

Concord Grape

Fruit Punch

Grape Peach

Mixed Fruit

Strawberry

White Grape Raspberry

Fruit Spread... see Jam/Jelly... see also Spread

G G

Gai Lan... *All Fresh Gai Lan Is Gluten/Casein/Soy Free*

Garbanzo Beans... see Beans

Garlic... *All Fresh Garlic Is Gluten/Casein/Soy Free*

   Earthbound Farm - Organic Chopped Garlic

   Trader Joe's - Crushed

Garlic Powder... see Seasonings

Garlic Salt... see Seasonings

Gelatin

   Hannaford Brand - Gelatin Fat Free (Cherry, Orange, Raspberry)

   Hy-Vee -

   Gelatin (Berry Blue, Cherry, Cranberry, Lemon, Lime, Orange,
      Raspberry, Strawberry, Strawberry Banana)

   Sugar Free (Cherry, Cranberry, Lime, Orange, Raspberry,
      Strawberry)

   Jell-O -

   Gelatin Snack Cups (Strawberry, Strawberry/Orange,
      Strawberry/Raspberry, Watermelon/Green Apple)

   Regular Instant (Apricot, Berry Blue, Black Cherry, Blackberry
      Fusion, Cherry, Cranberry, Grape, Island Pineapple, Lemon,
      Lime, Margarita, Melon Fusion, Mixed Fruit, Orange, Peach, Pina
      Colada, Raspberry, Strawberry (Banana, Daquiri, Kiwi, Regular),
      Tropical Fusion, Watermelon, Wild Strawberry)

   Sugar Free Low Calorie (Black Cherry, Cherry, Cranberry, Lemon,
      Lime, Mixed Fruit, Orange, Peach, Raspberry, Strawberry
      (Banana, Kiwi, Regular))

   Sugar Free Low Calorie Snack Cups (Cherry/Black Cherry,
      Orange/Lime, Peach/Watermelon, Raspberry/Orange,
      Strawberry, Strawberry Kiwi/Tropical Berry)

   Meijer Brand -

   Gelatin Dessert (Berry Blue, Cherry, Cranberry, Grape, Lime,
      Orange, Raspberry, Strawberry, Unflavored, Wild Strawberry)

Sugar Free Gelatin Dessert (Cherry, Cranberry, Lime, Orange, Raspberry, Strawberry)

Royal -

Regular (Blackberry, Cherry, Lime, Orange, Pineapple, Raspberry, Strawberry, Strawberry Banana, Raspberry)

Sugar Free (Cherry, Lime, Orange, Raspberry, Strawberry, Strawberry Banana)

Spartan Brand - Berry Blue, Cherry (Regular, Sugar Free), Lemon, Lime (Regular, Sugar Free), Orange (Regular, Sugar Free), Raspberry (Regular, Sugar Free), Strawberry (Regular, Sugar Free), Unflavored

Wegmans Brand - Sugar Free (Cherry & Black Cherry, Lemon Lime & Orange, Orange & Raspberry, Strawberry)

Gin... *All **Distilled** Alcohol Is **Gluten/Casein/Soy Free** [2]

Ginger

Lee Kum Kee - Minced Ginger

Wel-Pac - Sushi Ginger

Ginger Ale... see Soda Pop/Carbonated Beverages

Glaze

Daddy Sam's - Salmon Glaze

T. Marzetti - Fruit Glaze (Blueberry, Cranberry, Peach, Strawberry, Sugar Free Strawberry)

Graham Crackers

Jules Gluten Free▲ - Graham Cracker/Gingersnap Mix●

Grains

Arrowhead Mills - Amaranth, Hulled Millet, Quinoa

Bob's Red Mill▲ -

Organic Amaranth

Quinoa Organic

Teff Whole

Eden Organic - Brown Rice Flakes, Buckwheat, Millet, Quinoa, Red Quinoa, Wild Rice)

Shiloh Farms - Millet Grain, Quinoa, Red Quinoa, Sorghum Grain

G Granola

Bakery On Main - Gluten Free Granola (Apple Raisin Walnut, Cranberry Orange Cashew, Extreme Fruit & Nut, Nutty Maple Cranberry, Rainforest)

Enjoy Life▲ - Granola Crunch (Cinnamon●, Cranapple●, Very Berry●)

Gluten Free Sensations - Cherry Vanilla Almond, Cranberry Pecan, French Vanilla Almond

Goraw - Granola (Apple Cinnamon●, Live●, Live Chocolate●, Simple●)

Kookie Karma - All Varieties●

Rose's Bakery▲ - All Varieties●

Grapefruit... *All **Fresh** Grapefruit Is **Gluten/Casein/Soy Free***

Del Monte -

   Canned/Jarred Fruit (All Varieties)

   Fruit Snack Cups (Metal, Plastic)

Meijer Brand - Sections (In Juice, In Syrup)

Winn Dixie - Canned

Grapes... *All **Fresh** Grapes Are **Gluten/Casein/Soy Free***

Gravy/Gravy Mix

Barkat - Vegetable Gravy

Full Flavor Foods▲ - Gravy (Chicken●, Pork●, Turkey●)

Maxwell's Kitchen - Gravy Mix (Chicken, Turkey)

Orgran▲ - Gravy Mix

Green Beans... see Beans

Green Olives... see Olives

Green Peppers... *All **Fresh** Green Peppers Are **Gluten/Casein/Soy Free***

Green Tea... see Tea

Greens... *All **Fresh** Greens Are **Gluten/Casein/Soy Free***

Albertsons - Canned & Frozen Turnip Greens

Birds Eye - All Plain Frozen Collard Greens

G

Bush's Best - Chopped (Collard, Kale, Mixed, Mustard, Turnip, Turnip w/Diced Turnips)

C & W - All Plain Frozen Collard Greens

Laura Lynn - Canned (Chopped Collard Greens, Chopped Mustard Greens, Turnip Greens, Turnip Greens w/Diced Turnips), Mustard Greens

Lowes Foods Brand - Frozen (Chopped Collard, Turnip Greens)

Meijer Brand - Canned Chopped (Kale, Mustard, Turnip), Chopped (Collards, Kale, Mustard, Turnip)

Pictsweet - All Plain Frozen Collard Greens

Publix - Frozen (Collard Chopped, Turnip Chopped, Turnip w/Diced Turnips)

Spartan Brand - Chopped (Collard, Mustard)

Stop & Shop Brand - Collard Greens, Mustard Greens

Trader Joe's - All Plain Frozen Collard Greens

Winn Dixie -

Canned (Collard No Salt, Mustard, Turnip)

Frozen (Collard Greens Chopped, Mustard Greens, Steamable Mixed Vegetables)

Grits

Bob's Red Mill▲ - Gluten Free Corn Grits/Polenta

Meijer Brand - Quick

Groats

Arrowhead Mills - Buckwheat

Chateau Cream Hill Estates - Lara's Oat Groats●

Montana Monster Munchies - Raw & Sproutable Oat Groats●

Pocono - Whole Buckwheat

Ground Beef... see Beef

All Fresh Meat Is Gluten/Casein/Soy Free (Non-Marinated, Unseasoned)

Ground Turkey... see Turkey

All Fresh Poultry Is Gluten/Casein/Soy Free (Non-Marinated, Unseasoned)

G Guacamole... see also Dip/Dip Mix

Calavo

H Fischer & Wieser - Just Add Avocados Guacamole Starter

Guar Gum

Bob's Red Mill▲

El Peto▲

Gluten-Free Essentials▲

Kinnikinnick▲

Gum... see Chewing Gum

H

Halibut... see Fish

Ham

Applegate Farms - Natural (Black Forest, Honey, Slow Cooked), Organic Uncured Ham

Bar S -

Classic Chopped

Deli Shaved (Black Forest, Honey, Smoked)

Deli Style (Honey, Low Fat, Smoked)

Deli Thin Cut (Honey, Smoked)

Extra Lean Cooked

Steaks (Honey, Smoked)

Premium Deli (Honey, Smoked)

Black Label - Canned Hams

Boar's Head - 42% Lower Sodium, Sweet Slice Boneless, Virginia

Carl Buddig - All Ham *(Except Sandwich Kits)*

Celebrity - Boneless Cooked w/Natural Juices, Regular Ham

Cure 81 - Boneless Ham Natural Juices

Dietz & Watson -

Black Forest Smoked w/Natural Juices

Capocolla

Chef Carved Pre Sliced Honey Cured & Glazed

Classic Trimmed & Tied w/Natural Juices

Gourmet Lite (Tavern, Virginia Baked)

Ham Steak w/Natural Juices

Honey (Cured Dinner w/Natural Juices, Cured Tavern w/Natural Juices, Cured w/Natural Juices)

Imported (Prosciuttini Italian Style, w/Water Added)

Rosemary

Semi Boneless Smoked w/Natural Juices

Spiral Sliced

Tavern w/Water Added

Tomato & Basil

Tiffany Boneless w/Natural Juices

Virginia Baked w/Water Added

Garrett County Farms -

Black Forest Boneless Nugget

Deli (Black Forest, Virginia)

Sliced (Black Forest, Breakfast Virginia Brand (Boneless Ham Steak, Deli Ham), Turkey Ham (Ham Steak, Original))

Great Value Brand (Wal-Mart) -

Deli Meat

97% Fat Free (Baked Ham Water Added, Honey Ham Water Added)

Thinly Sliced Smoked (Ham, Honey Ham)

Healthy Choice - Honey

Hillshire Farms -

Deli Select Thin Sliced (Brown Sugar Baked Ham, Smoked Ham)

Deli Select Ultra Thin (Brown Sugar Baked Ham, Honey Ham)

H

Hormel -
> Black Label (Canned, Chopped)
> Chunk Meats Ham
> Deli Sliced (Black Forest, Cooked, Honey, Prosciutto)
> Diced
> Natural Choice Ham (Cooked Deli, Honey Deli, Smoked Deli)

Hy-Vee -
> Deli Thin Slices (Honey, Smoked)
> Thin Sliced (Ham w/Natural Juices, Honey Ham w/Natural Juices)

Isaly's - Chip Chopped, Old Fashioned Baked Deli, Smoked Honey Cured

Jennie-O - Refrigerated Turkey Ham (Extra Lean, Regular)

Jones Dairy Farm -
> Deli Style Ham Slices
>> Honey & Brown Sugar●
>> Old Fashioned Cured●
> Family Ham
>> Half●
>> Whole●
> Whole Fully Cooked Hickory Smoked●

Kayem - Deli Ham (Amber Honey Cured, Black Forest, Carving, Peppercrust)

Krakus - Imported Polish Ham

Meijer - Thin Sliced Ham Water Added 97% Fat Free (Cooked, Honey, Smoked)

Oscar Mayer -
> Deli Fresh Meats (Cooked Ham (96% Fat Free, Regular), Honey Ham, Smoked Ham)
> Shaved Deli Fresh Meats (Black Forest Ham, Brown Sugar Ham, Honey Ham, Smoked Ham, Virginia Brand Ham)
> Thin Sliced Deli Fresh (97% Fat Free Smoked Ham, Brown Sugar Ham)

Primo Taglio - Prosciutto Dry Cured Ham

Publix -

Deli Pre Pack Lunch Meat (Cooked Ham, Extra Thin Sliced Honey Ham, Low Salt Ham, Sweet Ham, Tavern Ham, Virginia Brand Ham)

Hickory Smoked Ham (Fully Cooked, Semi Boneless)

Honey Cured Ham w/Brown Sugar Glaze (Bone In Ham, Boneless Ham)

Russer - Reduced Sodium Cooked, Virginia

Safeway Brand - Boneless Honey

Smithfield -

Black Forest

Boneless Maple Flavored

Boneless Hickory

Boneless Honey

Cooked

Deli Thin Cooked

Deli Thin Honey

Virginia

SPAM - Classic, Less Sodium, Lite, Oven Roasted Turkey, Smoke Flavored

Spartan Brand - Frozen Ham Loaf, Whole Boneless

Underwood Spreads - Deviled

Wegmans Brand -

Diced Ham

Thin Shaved (Ham, Honey Maple Flavored Ham)

Wellshire Farms -

Black Forest (Boneless Nugget, Deli, Sliced)

Buffet Half

Glazed Boneless (Half, Spiral Sliced Half, Spiral Sliced Whole)

Old Fashioned Boneless (Half, Whole)

H

Semi Boneless (Half, Whole)

Sliced (Breakfast, Tavern)

Smoked Ham (Hocks, Shanks)

Top Round Ham Boneless

Turkey Half Ham

Virginia Brand (Boneless Steak, Buffet, Deli, Nugget Honey, Quarter, Sliced)

Winn Dixie - Thin Sliced (Cooked Ham, Honey Ham)

Hamburger Buns... see Buns

Hamburgers... see Burgers... *All Fresh Meat Is Gluten/Casein/Soy Free (Non-Marinated, Unseasoned)*

Hash Browns... see Potatoes

Hearts Of Palm... *All Fresh Hearts Of Palm Are Gluten/Casein/Soy Free*

Del Monte - All Plain Canned Hearts Of Palm

Native Forest - Organic Hearts Of Palm

Herbal Tea... see Tea

Hominy

Bush's Best - Golden, White

Great Value Brand (Wal-Mart) - Canned White

Hy-Vee - Golden, White

Lowes Foods Brand - White

Meijer Brand - White

Safeway Brand - Golden, White

Spartan Brand - Gold, White

Winn Dixie - Golden, White

Honey

Albertsons - Honey

Bramley's - Golden

Full Circle - Organic 100% Pure Honey

Great Value Brand (Wal-Mart) - Clover Honey

Hannaford Brand - Pure Clover
Home Harvest Brand - Pure Clover, Squeeze Bear
Hy-Vee - Honey, Honey Squeeze Bear
Lowes Foods Brand - Honey
Meijer Brand - Honey, Honey Squeeze Bear
Publix - Clover, Orange Blossom
Publix GreenWise Market - Organic Honey
Safeway Brand - Pure
Spartan Brand
Trader Joe's - Honey (All)
Virginia Brand - 100% All Natural
Wegmans Brand - 100% Pure Clover, Clover, Orange Blossom,
   Squeezable Bear
Winn Dixie - Clover, Dark, Orange Blossom
Honey Mustard Sauce... see Mustard
Horseradish Sauce
  Baxters
  Hy-Vee - Prepared Horseradish
  Lou's Famous - Horseradish (Creamy, Regular)
  Manischewitz - Creamy Wasabi, Original
  Wegmans Brand - Prepared Horseradish
Hot Chocolate Mix... see Cocoa Mix
Hot Dog Buns... see Buns
Hot Dogs... see Sausage
Hot Sauce
  Bone Suckin' - Habanero Sauce
  Frank's RedHot - Chile 'N Lime, Original, Xtra Hot
  Frontera - Hot Sauce (Chipotle, Habanero, Jalapeno, Red Pepper)
  Gifts Of Nature▲ - Sriracha Hot Sauce
  House Of Blues - Bayou Heat Hot Sauce

La Victoria - Jalapeno, Salsa Brava

Texas Pete - Garlic, Hotter Hot, Original

Trappey - Hot Sauce

Winn Dixie - Louisiana (Extra Hot, Hot)

Hummus

Athenos -

Hummus

Artichoke & Garlic

Black Olive

Greek Style

Original

Pesto

Roasted Eggplant

Roasted Garlic

Roasted Red Pepper

Spicy Three Pepper

NeoClassic Hummus

Original

Original w/Sesame Seeds & Parsley

Roasted Garlic w/Garlic & Parsley

Roasted Red Pepper w/Red Peppers & Parsley

Casbah Natural Foods - Hummus

Fantastic World Foods - Original Hummus

Tribe Mediterranean Foods - All Natural Hummus (All Varieties)

Wegmans -

Smoked Jalapeno

Traditional

Wild Garden - Black Olive, Fire Roasted Red Pepper, Jalapeno, Red Hot Chili Pepper, Roasted Garlic, Sundried Tomato, Sweet 2 Pepper, Traditional

I

Ice Cream... (includes Frozen Desserts, Frozen Yogurt, Sherbet, Sorbet)

Albertsons - Twin Pops

Chapman's - Sorbet (Orange, Rainbow, Raspberry)

Cool Fruits - Fruit Juice Freezers (Grape & Cherry, Sour Apple)

Dreyer's -

Fruit Bars

Grape

Lemonade

Lime

Strawberry

Tangerine

Variety Pack (Lime, Strawberry & Wildberry)

Variety Pack No Sugar Added (Black Cherry, Mixed Berry, Strawberry, Strawberry Kiwi, Tangerine & Raspberry)

Edy's -

Fruit Bars

Grape

Lemonade

Lime

Strawberry

Tangerine

Variety Pack (Lime, Strawberry & Wildberry)

Variety Pack No Sugar Added (Black Cherry, Mixed Berry, Strawberry, Strawberry Kiwi, Tangerine & Raspberry)

Fla-Vor-Ice - Freezer Bars (Regular, Sugar Free)

Hawaiian Punch - Freezer Bars

Hood - Frozen Novelty Items (Hoodsie Pops 6 Flavor Assortment Twin Pops)

Hy-Vee - Pops (Cherry, Grape, Orange, Root Beer)

Icee - Freezer Bars

Jelly Belly - Freezer (Bars, Pops)

Kool Pops - Freezer Bars

Meijer Brand -

Juice Stix

Party Pops (No Sugar Added Assorted, Orange/Cherry/Grape, RB/B/BR)

Red White & Blue Pops

Twin Pops

Minute Maid - Juice Bars

Natural Choice -

All Full Of Fruit Bars

All Sorbets

North Star -

Lotta Pops (Fruit, Juice, Regular, Sugar Free)

Pops (Assorted Twin, Banana Twin, Blue Raspberry Twin, Cherry Twin, Melon, Patriot Junior)

Otter Pops - Freezer Bars (Plus, Regular)

Philly Swirl -

Philly Swirl Sorbet/Italian Ice

Original Swirl Stix

Sugar Free Swirl Stix

Pop Ice - Freezer Bars

Publix -

Novelties

Banana Pops

Junior Ice Pops (Cherry, Grape, Orange)

Purely Decadent -

Coconut Milk Ice Cream

Chocolate●, Coconut●, Mocha Almond Fudge●, Passionate Mango●, Vanilla Bean●

I

Safeway Select -

Fruit Bars (Lemonade, Lime, Mandarin Orange, Strawberry)

Sorbet (Chocolate, Lemon, Mango, Peach, Pomegranate, Raspberry, Strawberry, Tropical)

So Delicious Dairy Free -

Kidz (Assorted Fruit Pops●, Fudge Pops●)

Sweet Nothings - Non Dairy (Fudge Bars●, Mango Raspberry●)

Tampico - All Freezer Bars

Wegmans Brand - Sorbet (Green Apple, Lemon, Pink Grapefruit, Raspberry)

Winn Dixie - Assorted Juice Pops, Assorted Junior Pops, Fun Pops, Red White & Blue Pops, Sugar Free Pops

Wyler's - Italian Ice Freezer Bars

Ice Cream Cones... see Cones

Ice Cream Toppings... see also Syrup

Hershey's - Chocolate Syrup (Lite, Regular, w/Calcium)

Maple Grove Farms Of Vermont -

Flavored Syrups

Apricot

Blueberry

Boysenberry

Raspberry

Strawberry

Smucker's -

Special Recipe (Triple Berry)

Sundae Syrups (Strawberry)

Toppings (Apple Cinnamon, Marshmallow, Pecans In Syrup, Pineapple, Strawberry, Walnuts In Syrup)

Iced Tea/Iced Tea Mix... see Tea

Icing... see Baking Decorations & Frostings

Instant Coffee... see Coffee

Italian Dressing... see Salad Dressing

J J

Jalapenos... *All Fresh Jalapenos Are Gluten/Casein/Soy Free*
  Chi-Chi's - Red
  Old El Paso - Slices (Pickled)
  Ortega - Hot (Sliced, Diced)
  Safeway Brand - Sliced
  Winn Dixie

Jalfrazi
  Seeds Of Change - Jalfrezi Sauce
  Sharwood's - Jalfrezi
  Tamarind Tree - Vegetable Jalfrazi

Jam/Jelly
  Baxters - Jelly (Cranberry, Mint, Red Currant)
  Bionaturae - Fruit Spread (Apricot, Bilberry, Peach, Plum, Raspberry, Sicilian Oranges, Sour Cherry, Strawberry, Wild Berry, Wild Blackberry)
  Cascadian Farm - Organic Fruit Spreads (Apricot, Blackberry, Blueberry, Concord Grape, Raspberry, Strawberry)
  Eden Organic - Butter (Apple, Cherry)
  Fischer & Wieser -
    Jelly Texas (Mild Green Jalapeno)
    Marmalade (Apricot Orange)
    Preserves
      Cinnamon Orange Tomato
      Old Fashioned Peach
      Southern Style Amaretto Peach Pecan
      Southern Style Jalapeno Peach
      Strawberry Rhubarb
  Food Club Brand - Grape Jam, Grape Jelly, Organic Fruit Spread (Apricot, Raspberry, Strawberry, Wild Blueberry), Preserves (Apricot, Peach, Strawberry)

J

Full Circle - Fruit Spread (Raspberry, Strawberry)

Hannaford Brand - Jelly (Apple, Currant, Grape, Strawberry), Orange Marmalade, Preserves (Apricots, Blueberry, Grape, Red Raspberry)

Hy-Vee -

Jelly (Apple, Blackberry, Cherry, Grape, Plum, Red Raspberry, Strawberry)

Orange Marmalade

Preserves (Apricot, Cherry, Concord Grape, Peach, Red Raspberry, Strawberry)

Laura Lynn -

Grape Jam

Jelly (Apple, Grape)

Orange Marmalade

Preserves (Apricot, Peach, Red Raspberry, Strawberry)

Lowes Foods Brand - Jam (Grape), Jelly (Apple, Grape), Preserves (Strawberry)

Meijer Brand - Fruit Spread (Apricot, Blackberry Seedless, Red Raspberry, Strawberry), Jam (Grape), Jelly (Grape), Preserves (Apricot, Blackberry Seedless, Marmalade Orange, Peach, Red Raspberry, Red Raspberry w/Seeds, Strawberry)

Midwest Country Fare - Grape Jelly, Strawberry Preserves

O Organics - Preserves (Apricot, Blackberry, Blueberry, Raspberry, Strawberry)

Polaner - All (Jam, Jellies, Preserves)

Publix - All (Jam, Jellies, Preserves)

Safeway Brand - All (Jams, Jellies, Preserves)

Safeway Select - All (Jams, Jellies, Preserves)

Smucker's - All (Jams, Jellies, Marmalades, Preserves)

Spartan Brand - Jam (Grape), Jelly (Apple, Currant, Grape, Strawberry), Orange Marmalade, Preserves (Apricot, Blackberry, Cherry, Peach, Red Raspberry, Strawberry)

J

Stop & Shop Brand -
Jelly (Apple, Currant, Mint)
Preserves (Apricot, Grape, Peach, Pineapple, Red Raspberry, Seedless Blackberry, Strawberry)

Walden Farms -
Spread
Apple Butter
Apricot
Blueberry
Grape
Orange Marmalade
Raspberry
Strawberry

Wegmans Brand -
Fruit Spread
Apricot/Peach/Passion Fruit
Blueberry/Cherry/Raspberry
Organic (Red Raspberry, Strawberry)
Raspberry/Strawberry/Blackberry
Strawberry/Plum/Raspberry
Jelly (Apple, Cherry, Concord Grape, Currant, Mint, Red Raspberry, Strawberry)
Nature's Marketplace Organic Fruit Spread Jammin' (Red Raspberry, Strawberry)
Preserves (Apricot, Cherry, Concord Grape, Peach, Red Raspberry, Seedless Blackberry, Strawberry)
Sugar Free Fruit Spread
Apricot/Peach/Passion Fruit
Raspberry/Wild Blueberry/Blackberry
Strawberry/Plum/Raspberry

Welch's - All Jams, Jellies & Preserves

Jell-O... see Gelatin

Jerky/Beef Sticks

   Applegate Farms - Joy Stick

   Garrett County - Turkey Tom Tom Snack Sticks

   Gary West

      Buffalo Strips

      Certified Angus Beef Steak Strips (All Varieties) *(Except Teriyaki)*

      Elk Strips

      Original Steak Strips (All Varieties) *(Except Teriyaki)*

   Hormel - Dried Beef

Juice... see Drinks/Juice

Juice Mix... see Drink Mix

K

Kale... *All Fresh Kale Is Gluten/Casein/Soy Free*

   Pictsweet - Cut Leaf

Kasha

   Bob's Red Mill▲ - Organic

   Shiloh Farms - Organic

   Wolff's - Buckwheat Kasha

Ketchup

   Great Value Brand (Wal-Mart)

   Hannaford Brand

   Heinz - Hot & Spicy, No Sodium Added, Organic, Reduced Sugar, Regular

   Hy-Vee - Thick & Rich Tomato (Regular, Squeezable)

   Meijer Brand - Regular, Squeeze, Tomato Organic

   Midwest Country Fare

   Muir Glen - Organic Tomato

   O Organics

   Organicville - Organic

K Publix
Publix GreenWise Market - Organic
L Safeway Brand
Walden Farms
Wegmans Brand - Organic
Winn Dixie - Organic, Regular
Woodstock Farms - Organic

Kielbasa... see Sausage

Kipper Snacks
  Crown Prince -
    Natural Naturally Smoked
    Regular Naturally Smoked
  Ocean Prince -
    In Mustard
    Naturally Smoke

Kiwi... *All Fresh Kiwi Is Gluten/Casein/Soy Free*

Kohlrabi... *All Fresh Kohlrabi Is Gluten/Casein/Soy Free*

Korma
  Amy's - Indian Vegetable

L

Lamb... *All Fresh Meat Is Gluten/Casein/Soy Free (Non-Marinated, Unseasoned)*

Lasagna Noodles... see Pasta

Lemonade... see Drinks/Juice

Lemons... *All Fresh Lemons Are Gluten/Casein/Soy Free*
  Sunkist

L

M

Lentils... see also Beans

    Tasty Bite - Bengal, Jaipur Vegetables

Lettuce... *All Fresh Lettuce Is Gluten/Casein/Soy Free*

Licorice... see Candy/Candy Bars

Limeade... see Drinks/Juice

Limes... *All Fresh Limes Are Gluten/Casein/Soy Free*

    Sunkist

Liverwurst

    Jones Dairy Farm -

        Chub Braunschweiger Liverwurst (Bacon & Onion●, Light●, Mild & Creamy●, Original●)

        Chunk Braunschweiger (Light●, Original●)

        Sliced Braunschweiger●

        Stick Braunschweiger●

Lobster... *All Fresh Shellfish Is Gluten/Casein/Soy Free (Non-Marinated, Unseasoned)*

Lunch Meat... see Deli Meat

M

Macaroni & Cheese

    Ian's - Wheat Free Gluten Free Mac & No Cheese

    Namaste Foods▲ - Say Cheez

    Road's End Organics -

        Dairy Free Mac & Chreese Alfredo

        Dairy Free Penne & Chreese

Macaroons... see Cookies

Mackerel... see also Fish... *All Fresh Fish Is Gluten/Casein/Soy Free (Non-Marinated, Unseasoned)*

    Chicken Of The Sea - Canned Jack Mackerel

    Crown Prince - Jack Mackerel

M Makhani

    Tamarind Tree - Dal Makhani

  Mandarin Oranges... *All **Fresh** Mandarin Oranges Are **Gluten/ Casein/ Soy Free***

    Albertsons

    Del Monte -

        Canned/Jarred Fruit (All Varieties)

        Fruit Snack Cups (Metal, Plastic)

    Dole - All Fruits (Bowls, Canned, Dried, Frozen, Jars) *(Except Real Fruit Bites)*

    Food Club Brand

    Great Value Brand (Wal-Mart) - In Light Syrup

    Hannaford Brand - In Light Syrup

    Hy-Vee - Light Syrup, Orange Gel Cups, Regular Cups

    Kroger Brand - Fruit (Canned, Cups)

    Lowes Foods Brand - In Lite Syrup

    Meijer Brand - Light Syrup

    Publix - In Light Syrup

    Spartan Brand - Fruit Cups

    Trader Joe's - In Light Syrup

    Wegmans Brand - Regular, Whole Segment In Light Syrup

    Winn Dixie

  Mango... *All **Fresh** Mangos Are **Gluten/Casein/Soy Free***

    Del Monte -

        Canned/Jarred Fruit (All Varieties)

        Fruit Snack Cups (Metal, Plastic)

    Meijer Brand - Frozen (Chunks, Sliced)

    Native Forest - Organic Mango Chunks

    Stop & Shop Brand - Mango

    Winn Dixie - Frozen Mango Chunks

    Woodstock Farms - Organic Frozen Mango

M

Maple Syrup... see Syrup
Maraschino Cherries... see Cherries
Margarine... see Spread and/or Butter
Marinades
  Drew's All Natural -
    Garlic Italian
    Green Olive & Caper
    Honey Dijon
    Poppy Seed
    Raspberry
    Roasted Garlic & Peppercorn
    Rosemary Balsamic
    Smoked Tomato
  Jack Daniel's EZ Marinades - Original No. 7 Recipe
  Lawry's -
    Baja Chipotle
    Caribbean Jerk
    Havana Garlic & Lime
    Herb & Garlic
    Lemon Pepper
    Louisiana Red Pepper
    Mesquite
    Mexican Chile & Lime
  McCormick -
    Grill Mates
      Baja Citrus Marinade
      Chipotle Pepper Marinade
      Hickory BBQ Marinade
      Mesquite Marinade
      Mojito Lime

M

    Montreal Steak Marinade (25% Less Sodium, Original)

    Peppercorn & Garlic Marinade

    Southwest Marinade

Mr. Spice Organic - Sauce & Marinade (Ginger Stir Fry, Honey BBQ, Indian Curry, Sweet & Sour, Thai Peanut)

Weber Grill Creations - Chipotle Marinade

Winn & Lovett - Argentina, Cilantro Lime, Citrus, Garlic, Red Chili & Thyme

Winn Dixie - Mojo

Marmalade... see Jam/Jelly

Marshmallow Dip

    Jet Puffed - Marshmallow Crème

    Marshmallow Fluff - Original

    Walden Farms - Calorie Free Marshmallow Dip

Marshmallows

    Albertsons - Mini, Regular

    AllerEnergy

    Great Value Brand (Wal-Mart) - Regular

    Hannaford Brand - Miniature, Regular

    Hy-Vee - Colored Miniature, Miniature, Regular

    Jet-Puffed - Coconut, Funmallows, Miniatures, Regular, Strawberrymallows, Swirlmallows Caramel & Vanilla, Vanilla

    Marshmallow Fluff - Original

    Meijer Brand - Mini, Mini Flavored, Regular

    Publix

    Safeway Brand - Large, Mini

    Spartan Brand - Miniature, Regular

    Winn Dixie - Mini, Regular

Masala

    Tamarind Tree - Channa Dal Masala

    Tasty Bite - Channa Masala

M

Mashed Potatoes

Edward & Sons - Organic (Home Style, Roasted Garlic)

Meijer Brand - Instant Mashed Potatoes

Ore-Ida - Steam N' Mash (Cut Red, Cut Russet, Cut Sweet)

Safeway Brand - Instant Mashed Potatoes (Regular)

Spartan Brand - Instant

Mayonnaise

Simply Delicious - Organic Mayonnaise (Garlic, Lemon, Original)

Spectrum - Canola Mayonnaise

Walden Farms - Mayo

Meals

A Taste Of Thai - Quick Meal (Vermicelli Rice Noodles)

Allegaroo▲ - Chili Mac, Spaghetti, Spyglass Noodles

Chi-Chi's - Fiesta Chicken Salsa Plate

Dinty Moore - Microwave Meals (Chicken w/ Rice)

Gillian's Foods▲ - Chicken Cutlets

Glutino▲ - Frozen Meals (Chicken Ranchero, Pomodoro Chicken)

Hormel - Compleats (Santa Fe Style Chicken), Compleats Microwave 10 oz. Meals (Chicken & Rice, Santa Fe Style Chicken w/Beans & Rice)

Ian's - Wheat Free Gluten Free (Mac & Meat Sauce, Mac & No Cheese)

Kid's Kitchen - Beans & Wieners

Mixes From The Heartland▲ -

Meal Mix

BBQ Beef N'Pasta●

Beef Skillet●

Cheeseburger Pie●

Garden Meat Loaf●

Green Chili●

Green Chili Spaghetti●

M

    Mexican Chicken N' Rice●
    Mexican Style Casserole●
    Sausage Casserole●
    Southwest Potato Casserole●
    Taco Rice Skillet●
    Tex Mex Meat Loaf●
    Tex Mex Spaghetti●
    Texas Bean Bake●
    Texas Goulash●

My Own Meals -
    Beef Stew
    Chicken & Black Bean
    Mediterranean Chicken Meal
    My Kind Of Chicken
    Old World Stew

Namaste Foods▲ - Pasta Meals (Pasta Pisavera, Say Cheez, Taco)

Orgran▲ - Pasta Ready Meal (Tomato & Basil, Vegetable Bolognese), Spaghetti In A Can

Smart Ones - Frozen Entrees (Chicken Santa Fe)

Tasty Bite -
    Aloo Palak
    Bombay Potatoes
    Mushroom Takatak
    Punjab Eggplant
    Spinach Dal & Basmati Rice

Thai Kitchen -
    Stir Fry Rice Noodle Meal Kit (Original Pad Thai)
    Take Out Box (Ginger & Sweet Chili, Original Pad Thai, Thai Basil & Chili)

Melon... *All **Fresh** Melons Are **Gluten/Casein/Soy Free***

Milk Alternative

M

Amazake -
  Almond Shake
  Amazing Mango
  Banana Appeal
  Chocolate Almond
  Cool Coconut
  Gimme Green
  Go Go Green
  Go Hazelnuts
  Oh So Original
  Rice Nog
  Tiger Chai
  Vanilla Pecan Pie

Dari Free - Non Dairy Milk Alternative (Chocolate, Original)

Good Karma - Organic Ricemilk (Chocolate, Original, Vanilla)

MimicCreme - Sugar Free Sweetened, Sweetened, Unsweetened

Pacific Natural Foods -
  All Natural Hazelnut Original
  Low Fat Rice Beverage (Plain, Vanilla)
  Organic Almond (Chocolate, Original, Vanilla, Unsweetened)

Rice Dream - Refrigerated & Shelf Stable Rice Beverages (All Varieties)

Wegmans Brand - Organic (Original, Vanilla)

Millet

Arrowhead Mills - Hulled Millet, Millet Flour

Bob's Red Mill▲ - Flour, Grits/Meal, Hulled Millet

Mints... see also Candy/Candy Bars

Altoids - Large Tins (Peppermint, Wintergreen)

Safeway Brand - Dessert, Star Light

Vermints - Café Express, Chai, Cinnamint, Gingermint, Peppermint, Wintermint

M Mixed Fruit... *All Fresh Mixed Fruit Is Gluten/Casein/Soy Free*

Cascadian Farm - Organic Frozen Tropical Fruit Blend

Del Monte -

Canned/Jarred Fruit (All Varieties)

Fruit Snack Cups (Metal, Plastic)

Dole - All Fruits (Bowls, Canned, Dried, Frozen, Jars) *(Except Real Fruit Bites)*

Food Club Brand - Frozen Berry Medley, Triple Cherry Mixed Fruit (Fruit Cups)

Great Value Brand (Wal-Mart) -

Canned (Triple Cherry Fruit Mix In Natural Flavored Cherry Light Syrup, Tropical Fruit Salad in Light Syrup & Fruit Juices)

Frozen (Berry Medley)

Hannaford Brand - Light Syrup, No Sugar Added Chunky, Triple Cherry Light Syrup

Home Harvest Brand

Hy-Vee - Fruit Cups (Mixed, Tropical), Mixed Fruit (Lite Chunk, Regular)

Laura Lynn - Canned

Lowes Foods Brand - Canned Fruit Cocktail (In Heavy Syrup, In Juice)

Meijer Brand - Frozen Tropical Fruit Blend, Mixed Fruit (Individually Quick Frozen, Regular)

Publix -

Canned (Chunky Mixed Fruit In Heavy Syrup, Fruit Cocktail In Heavy Syrup, Lite Chunky Mixed Fruit In Pear Juice)

Frozen (Mixed Fruit)

S&W - All Canned/Jarred Fruits

Spartan Brand - Frozen (Berry Medley, Mixed Fruit), In Heavy Syrup

Stop & Shop Brand - Fruit Mix In Heavy Syrup, Mixed Fruit, Very Cherry Fruit Mix In Light Syrup

Wegmans Brand - Fruit Cocktail (In Heavy Syrup, In Pear Juice, Regular)

Winn Dixie - Canned Chunky Mixed Fruit (Heavy Syrup, Light Syrup), Frozen (Berry Medley, Mixed Fruit), Fruit Cocktail (Heavy Syrup, Light Syrup)

M

Woodstock Farms - Tropical Fruit Mix

Mixed Vegetables... *All Fresh Mixed Vegetabls Are Gluten/Casein/ Soy Free (Except w/Soybeans)*

Albertsons - Canned, Frozen *(Except Sweet Onion Rounds, w/Edamame)*

Birds Eye - All Plain Frozen Vegetables *(Except w/Edamame)*

C & W - All Plain Frozen Vegetables *(Except w/Edamame)*

Cascadian Farm - Organic Frozen (California Style Blend, Gardener's Blend)

Del Monte - All Plain Canned Vegetables *(Except w/Edamame)*

Food Club Brand - Canned Mixed Vegetables, Frozen (California Style, Italian Style, Florentine Style, Mixed Vegetables)

Freshlike - All Frozen Plain Vegetables *(Except w/Edamame)*

Full Circle - Organic Frozen 4 Vegetable Blend

Grand Selections - Frozen Vegetables (Caribbean Blend)

Great Value Brand (Wal-Mart) -
    Canned (Mixed Vegetables, Vegetable Medley)
    Frozen Vegetable Mix (California Style, Italian Style)

Green Giant - Frozen Mixed Vegetables

Hannaford Brand - Mixed Vegetables

Home Harvest Brand - Mixed Vegetables (Canned, Frozen)

Hy-Vee -
    Canned Mixed Vegetables
    Frozen
        California Mix
        Country Trio
        Feast Blend
        Mixed Vegetables
        Oriental Vegetables
        Stew Vegetables

Kroger Brand - All Plain Vegetables (Canned, Frozen) *(Except w/Soybeans)*

M

Lowes Foods Brand - Frozen (California Blend, Fajita Blend, Italian Blend, Mixed Vegetables, Peking Stir Fry, Vegetables For Soup)

Meijer Brand -

Canned Mixed

Frozen

California Style

Fiesta

Florentine

Italian

Mexican

Mixed Vegetables (Organic, Regular)

Oriental

Parisian Style

Stew Mix

Stir Fry

Midwest Country Fare - Canned, Frozen (California Blend, Mixed Vegetables, Winter Mix)

O Organics - Frozen (California Style Vegetables, Mixed Vegetable Blend)

Pictsweet - All Plain Frozen Vegetables *(Except w/Edamame)*

Publix -

Canned Mixed

Frozen Blends

Alpine

California

Del Oro

Gumbo

Italian

Japanese

Mixed Vegetable

Peas & Carrots

M

Roma

Soup Mix w/Tomatoes

Succotash

S&W - All Canned Vegetables *(Except Soybeans)*

Safeway Brand - Frozen Blends (Asian Style, California Style, Santa Fe Style, Stew Vegetables, Stir Fry, Tuscan Style Vegetables, Winter Blend), Mixed Vegetables (Canned, Frozen)

Spartan Brand - Canned Mixed Vegetables, Frozen (Baby Pea Blend, Baby Corn Blend, California Vegetables, Fiesta Vegetables, Italian Vegetables, Mixed Vegetables, Oriental Vegetables, Pepper Stirfry, Stew Mix Vegetables, Vegetables For Soup, Winter Blend)

Stop & Shop Brand -

Country Blend

Latino Blend

Mixed Vegetables (No Added Salt, Regular)

Stew Vegetables

Tasty Bite - Kerala Vegetables

Trader Joe's - All Plain Frozen Vegetables *(Except w/Edamame)*

Wegmans Brand -

Mix (Santa Fe, Southern, Spring)

Mixed Vegetables (Canned, Frozen)

Winn Dixie - Canned No Salt Added, Frozen Mixed Vegetables (Organic, Regular)

Woodstock Farms - Organic Frozen Plain Mixed Vegetables *(Except Edamame)*

Molasses

Brer Rabbit - Molasses (Blackstrap, Full Flavor, Mild)

Grandma's - Original, Robust

Publix

Mousse

Orgran▲ - Chocolate Mousse Mix

M Muffins/Muffin Mix

1-2-3 Gluten Free▲ - Meredith's Marvelous Muffin/Quickbread●

Aunt Gussie's▲ - English Muffins (Cinnamon Raisin, Original)

Authentic Foods▲ - Blueberry Muffin Mix

Breads From Anna▲ - Pancake & Muffin Mix (Apple, Cranberry, Maple)

Cause You're Special▲ - Classic Muffin & Quickbread Mix, Lemon Poppy Seed Muffin Mix, Sweet Corn Muffin Mix

El Peto▲ - Sugar Free Muffins (Banana, Blueberry, Carrot, Raisin/Rice Bran)

Ener-G▲ - Brown Rice English Muffins w/Flax, English Muffins

Flour Nut - Muffin Mix (Austin's Maple Cinnamon, Maple Walnut)

Foods By George▲ - Muffins (Cinnamon Currant English, English, No-Rye Rye English)

Gluten Free Life▲ - The Ultimate Gluten Free Cake Muffin & Brownie Mix

Gluten-Free Creations▲ - Chocolate Zucchini●, Cranberry Orange Pecan●, English Muffins●, Lemon Poppyseed●

Gluten-Free Essentials▲ -
  Lemon Poppy Seed Bread & Muffin Mix
  Spice Cake & Muffin Mix

Hodgson Mill▲ - Apple Cinnamon Muffin Mix

Kinnikinnick▲ - Blueberry, Carrot, Cranberry, Tapioca Rice English Muffin

Namaste Foods▲ - Muffin Mix, Sugar Free

Only Oats - Muffin Mix (Cinnamon Spice●)

Orgran▲ - Muffin Mix (Chocolate, Lemon & Poppyseed)

Pitter Patties - Viva Vegan, Yammy Chicken

Simply Organic - Chai Spice Scone Mix●

The Really Great Food Company▲ - Muffin Mix (Apple Spice, Cornbread English, Maple Raisin, Sweet, Vanilla)

M

Mushrooms... *All Fresh Mushrooms Are Gluten/Casein/Soy Free*

   Albertsons - Pieces & Stems (No Salt, Regular)

   Eden Organic - Maitake (Dried), Shiitake (Dried Sliced, Dried Whole)

   Food Club Brand - Canned (Pieces & Stems, Whole)

   Great Value Brand (Wal-Mart) - Canned Mushrooms Pieces & Stems

   Green Giant - Canned/Jarred (Pieces & Stems, Sliced, Whole)

   Hannaford Brand - Stems & Pieces (No Salt, Regular)

   Hy-Vee - Sliced, Stems & Pieces

   Lowes Foods Brand - Jar (Sliced, Whole)

   Meijer Brand - Canned (Sliced, Whole), Canned Stems & Pieces (No Salt, Regular)

   Midwest Country Fare - Mushrooms & Stems (No Salt Added, Regular)

   Pennsylvania Dutchman - Sliced, Stems & Pieces, Whole

   Publix - Sliced, Stems & Pieces

   Safeway Brand - Canned (Button Sliced)

   Wegmans Brand - Button, Pieces & Stems, Sliced

   Woodstock Farms - Organic Frozen (Mixed, Shiitake)

Mustard

   Annie's Naturals - Organic (Dijon, Honey, Horseradish, Yellow)

   Best Foods - Deli Brown, Honey

   Bone Suckin' - Sweet Hot

   Di Lusso - Chipotle, Cranberry Honey, Deli Style, Dijon, Honey, Jalapeno

   Dietz & Watson - Champagne Dill, Jalapeno, Stone Ground, Sweet & Hot, Wasabi, Whole Grain Dijon

   Eden Organic - Organic (Brown, Yellow)

   Emeril's - Dijon (Kicked Up Horseradish, NY Deli Style, Smooth Honey, Yellow)

   Fischer & Wieser -

      Smokey Mesquite

      Sweet Heat

      Sweet Sour & Smokey Sauce

French's - Classic Yellow, Honey, Honey Dijon, Horseradish, Spicy Brown

Frontera - Chipotle Honey Mustard Grilling Sauce

Great Value Brand (Wal-Mart) - Coarse Ground, Dijon, Honey, Southwest Spicy, Spicy Brown, Yellow

Grey Poupon - Country Dijon, Deli, Dijon, Harvest Coarse Ground, Hearty Spicy Brown, Savory Honey

Guldens - Natural Yellow, Spicy Brown, Zesty Honey

Hannaford Brand - Dijon, Honey, Spicy Brown, Yellow

Heinz - Dijon, Spicy Brown

Hellmann's - Deli Brown, Honey

Hy-Vee - Dijon, Honey, Regular, Spicy Brown

Jack Daniel's - Hickory Smoke, Honey Dijon, Horseradish, Old No. 7, Spicy Southwest, Stone Ground Dijon

Lou's Famous - Hot Mustard w/Horseradish

Meijer Brand - Honey Squeeze, Hot & Spicy, Salad Squeeze, Spicy Brown Squeeze

O Organics - Dijon, Yellow

Publix - Classic Yellow, Deli Style, Dijon, Honey, Spicy Brown

Publix GreenWise Market - Creamy Yellow, Spicy Yellow, Tangy Dijon

Safeway Brand - Coarse Ground Dijon, Dijon, Honey Mustard, Spicy Brown, Stone Ground Horseradish, Sweet & Spicy

Spartan Brand - Dijon, Honey, Prepared, Spicy Brown, Sweet & Hot

Texas Pete - Honey Mustard

Wegmans Brand - Classic Yellow, Dijon (Traditional), Horseradish, Smooth & Tangy, Spicy Brown

Winn Dixie - Yellow

Woodstock Farms - Dijon, Stone Ground, Yellow

Mutter

Tamarind Tree - Dhingri Mutter

nutritional supplements

N   N

Nectars

> **Bionaturae** - Organic (Apple, Apricot, Bilberry, Carrot Apple, Peach, Pear, Plum, Sicilian Lemon, Sour Cherry, Strawberry, Wildberry)

Noodles... see also Pasta

> **A Taste Of Thai** - Rice Noodles (Regular, Thin, Wide)
>
> **Annie Chun's** - Rice Noodles (Maifun, Pad Thai)
>
> **Mixes From The Heartland** - Noodle Mix (Plain, Spinach)
>
> **Seitenbacher** - Gourmet Noodles Gluten Free Golden Ribbon, Gluten Free Rigatoni
>
> **Sharwood's** - Rice Noodles
>
> **Thai Kitchen** - Rice Noodles (Stir Fry Rice Noodles, Thin Rice Noodles)

Nut Beverages

> **Pacific Natural Foods** - All Natural Hazelnut Original, Organic Almond (Chocolate, Original, Vanilla, Unsweetened)
>
> **MimicCreme** - Sugar Free Sweetened, Sweetened, Unsweetened

Nut Butter... see Peanut Butter

Nutritional Supplements

> **MLO** - Brown Rice Protein Powder
>
> **Odwalla** -
>
> > All Natural Carrot Juice
> >
> > All Natural Lemonade
> >
> > All Natural Orange Juice
> >
> > All Natural Smoothie (Mango Tango, Strawberry Banana)
> >
> > B Monster (Blueberry B)
> >
> > C Monster (Citrus C, Strawberry C)
> >
> > Mo' Beta
> >
> > Mojito Mambo
> >
> > Pomegranate Strawberry

N

    Serious Energy (Tropical Energy)

    Serious Focus (Apple Raspberry)

    Wholly Grain (Tropical Medley)

Ruth's - Organic Hemp Protein Powder (E3Live & Maca, Hemp Protein Power, Hemp w/Sprouted Flax & Maca)

Salba●

Nuts

Albertsons -

    Cashews (Halves & Pieces, Lightly Salted, Whole)

    Mixed Nuts (Deluxe, Lightly Salted, Regular)

    Peanuts (Lightly Salted Party, Party)

Frito Lay -

    Cashews

    Deluxe Mixed Nuts

    Honey Roasted (Cashews, Peanuts)

Great Value Brand (Wal-Mart) - Premium Pistachio

Hannaford Brand -

    Almonds (Natural, Roasted & Salted)

    Cashews Whole Lightly Salted

    Dry Roasted Peanuts

    Macadamia Dry Roasted

    Pistachio Kernels

Hy-Vee -

    Almonds (Dry Roasted, Honey Roasted, Natural, Raw, Roasted & Salted, Roasted Unsalted)

    Black Walnuts

    Cashews (Halves & Pieces, Honey Roasted, Sea Salted, w/Almonds, Whole, Whole Lightly Salted)

    English Walnut Pieces

    English Walnuts

    Macadamia

N

Mixed Nuts (Deluxe Lightly Salted, Deluxe No Peanuts, Lightly Salted, Regular, w/Pistachios)

Natural Almonds (Regular, Sliced)

Peanuts (Dry Roasted Unsalted, Honey Roasted, Party)

Pecan (Pieces, Regular)

Raw Spanish Peanuts

Salted Peanuts (Blanched, Spanish)

Slivered Almonds

Katy Sweet▲ - Nuts (Glazed Pecans, Holy Mole, Peppered Pecans, Sugar & Spice Pecans)

Mareblu Naturals -

Crunch (Almond, Almond Coconut, Cashew, Cashew Coconut, CranMango Cashew, Pecan Cinnamon, Pistachio)

Trail Mix Crunch (Blueberry Pomegranate, Cranberry Pomegranate, Cranblueberry Trail, Cranstrawberry Trail, Pecan Trail, Pistachio Trail)

Meijer Brand -

Almonds (Blanched Sliced, Blanched Slivered, Natural Sliced, Slivered, Whole)

Cashews (Halves w/Pieces, Halves w/Pieces Lightly Salted, Whole)

Mixed (Deluxe, Lightly Salted, Regular)

Nut Topping

Peanuts

Blanched (Regular, Slightly Salted)

Dry Roasted (Lightly Salted, Regular, Unsalted)

Honey Roasted

Spanish

Pecan (Chips, Halves)

Pine

Walnuts (Black, Chips, Halves & Pieces)

N Nut Harvest -
  Natural
    Honey Roasted Peanuts
    Lightly Roasted Almonds
    Nut & Fruit Mix
    Sea Salted Peanuts
    Sea Salted Whole Cashews
Planters - Cashews Halves & Pieces, Dry Roasted Peanuts, Extra
  Large Virginia Peanuts, Fancy Whole Cashews, Honey Roasted
  Peanuts, Mixed Nuts, Pistachio Lovers Mix
Publix -
  Almonds (Natural Whole, Sliced)
  Macadamia
  Peanuts (Dry Roasted Lightly Salted, Dry Roasted Salted, Dry
    Roasted Unsalted, Premium Salted Jumbo)
  Pecan Halves
  Walnuts
Safeway Brand -
  Almonds (Roasted & Salted, Smoked Flavored, Whole Natural)
  Honey Roasted Party Peanuts
  Mixed (Deluxe, Regular)
  Nuts Cashews (Halves, Pieces, Whole)
Spartan Brand - Dry Roasted Peanuts (Regular), Lightly Salted Dry
  Roasted Peanuts, No Salt Dry Roasted Peanuts
Sunkist - Gourmet Oven Roasted Almonds, Pistachios (Dry Roasted,
  Kernels)
True North - Almond Pistachios Walnuts Pecans, Clusters (Almond,
  Pecan Almond Peanut)
Wegmans Brand -
  Dry Roasted (Macadamias, Seasoned Peanuts)
  Natural Whole Almonds

Peanuts Dry Roasted (Lightly Salted, Seasoned, Unsalted)

Peanuts (Salted In The Shell, Unsalted In The Shell)

Pine Nuts (Italian Classics)

Winn & Lovett - Coconut Almonds

Winn Dixie -

Cashews (Honey Roasted)

Peanuts (Dry Roasted Lightly Salted, Dry Roasted Salted, Dry Roasted Unsalted, Green Boiled)

Roasted Pistachios

Woodstock Farms -

Nuts

Almonds (Non Pareil, Roasted & No Salt, Roasted & Salt, Supreme, Thick Sliced)

Brazil

Cashew (Large Whole (Regular, Roasted))

Deluxe Mixed Nuts Roasted

Extra Fancy Mixed Nuts

Hazelnut Filberts

Peanuts Honey Roasted

Pecan Halves

Pine

Walnuts Halves & Pieces

Organic Nuts

Almonds

Brazil

Cashews (Large Whole (Regular, Roasted & Salt), Pieces)

Pecan Halves

Pine

Pistachios (No Salt, Roasted & Salt)

Walnuts Halves & Pieces

OO

Oatmeal

Glutenfreeda▲ - Instant Oatmeal (Apple Cinnamon w/Flax, Banana w/Flax, Maple Raisin w/Flax, Natural)

Oats

Bob's Red Mill▲ - Gluten Free Rolled Oats

Chateau Cream Hill Estates - Lara's Rolled Oats●

Gifts Of Nature▲ - Old Fashioned Rolled Oats●, Whole Oat Groats

Gluten-Free Oats▲ - Old Fashioned Rolled Oats●

Montana Monster Munchies - Whole Grain (Grab & Go●, Quick Oats●, Rolled Oats●)

Only Oats - Steel Cut Oat Pearls●

Oil

Albertsons - All Oil (*Except Vegetable Oil*)

Annie's Naturals -

Olive Oil (Basil, Dipping, Roasted Pepper)

Olive Oil Extra Virgin (Roasted Garlic)

Bertolli - All Olive Oils

Bionaturae - Organic Extra Virgin Olive Oil

Bragg - Organic (Extra Virgin Olive Oil, Olive Oil)

Carapelli - Olive Oil

Crisco - 100% Pure Extra Virgin Olive, Light Olive, Pure (Canola, Corn, Olive, Peanut), Puritan Canola w/Omega 3DHA

Eden Organic -

Olive Oil Spanish Extra Virgin

Organic (Hot Pepper Sesame Oil, Safflower Oil, Sesame Oil Extra Virgin)

Toasted Sesame Oil

Food Club Brand - Canola, Corn

Full Circle - Organic (Canola, Extra Virgin Olive Oil)

Grand Selections - 100% Pure & Natural Olive Oil, Extra Light, Extra Virgin Olive Oil, Olive Oil (Basil, Chili, Garlic, Lemon)

Great Value Brand (Wal-Mart) - Olive Oil (Extra Virgin, Light Tasting), Pure Oil (Canola, Corn)

Hannaford Brand - Canola Oil, Corn Oil, Olive (Extra Virgin, Extra Virgin Imported, Light, Pure)

House Of Tsang - Oil (Hot Chili Sesame, Mongolian Fire, Sesame, Wok)

Hy-Vee -
100% Pure Oil (Canola, Corn)

Kroger Brand - Canola, Corn, Olive

Laura Lynn - Canola, Corn, Peanut

Lee Kum Kee - Pure Sesame

Lowes Foods Brand - 100% Pure Olive, Canola, Corn, Extra Virgin Olive, Peanut

Manitoba Harvest - Hemp Seed Oil (Organic, Regular)

Mazola - Canola, Cooking, Corn

Meijer Brand - Canola, Corn, Olive (100% Pure-Italian Classic, Extra Virgin (Italian Classic, Regular), Italian Select Premium Extra Virgin, Milder Tasting, Regular), Olive Infused (Garlic & Basil Italian, Roasted Garlic Italian, Spicy Red Pepper Italian), Sunflower, Peanut

Member's Mark - 100% Pure Olive Oil

Newman's Own Organics - Extra Virgin Olive Oil

Nutiva - Organic (Extra Virgin Coconut Oil, Hemp Oil)

O Organics - Extra Virgin Olive Oil

Oskri Organics - Extra Virgin Olive Oil, Flaxseed Oil, Grapeseed Oil, Omega 3 Olive Oil, Sesame Seed Oil

Publix - Oil (Canola, Corn, Extra Virgin, Light Olive, Olive, Peanut, Pure Italian Olive)

Ruth's - Certified Organic Hemp Oil

Safeway Brand - Canola, Corn

Safeway Select - Olive Oil (Extra Light, Extra Virgin, Regular)

O

Simply Enjoy - Apulian Regional Extra Virgin Olive Oil (Apulian, Sicilian, Tuscan, Umbrian)

Spartan Brand - Canola, Corn, Olive (Extra Virgin, Regular)

Spectrum Organic Products -

Almond Refined

Apricot Kernel Refined

Avocado Refined

Canola (High Heat, Organic Refined, Regular)

Coconut Organic (Refined, Unrefined)

Corn Unrefined

Grapeseed Refined

Olive Oil (All Varieties)

Peanut Unrefined

Safflower (Organic High Heat Refined, Regular High Heat, Unrefined)

Sesame (Organic Unrefined, Organic Unrefined Toasted, Refined, Regular, Unrefined Toasted)

Sunflower Organic High Heat Refined

Walnut Refined

Star -

Extra (Light, Virgin)

Originale

Stop & Shop Brand - Canola, Corn, Extra Light Olive, Pure Olive

Tassos - Olive Oil (Extra Virgin, Fine, Organic Extra, Peza Crete Extra)

Wegmans Brand -

Basting w/Garlic & Herbs

Canola

Corn

Extra Virgin (Black Truffle, Campania Style, Regular, Sicilian Lemon, Sicilian Style, Tuscany Style)

Grapeseed

O

  Mild Olive
  Organic (Extra Virgin Olive, Sunflower Oil)
  Peanut
  Pumpkin Seed
  Pure
Winn & Lovett - Extra Virgin Olive Oil
Winn Dixie - Canola, Corn, Olive, Peanut
Okra... *All Fresh Okra Is Gluten/Casein/Soy Free*
  Albertsons - Frozen (Cut, Whole)
  Lowes Foods Brand - Cut
  Meijer Brand - Frozen (Chopped, Whole)
  Pictsweet - All Plain Frozen Okra
  Publix - Frozen (Cut, Whole Baby)
  Safeway Brand - Frozen
  Spartan Brand - Cut, Whole
  Winn Dixie - Frozen (Cut, Diced, Whole)
  Woodstock Farms - Organic Frozen Cut Okra
Olive Oil... see Oil
Olives
  Albertsons
  Di Lusso - Green Ionian, Mediterranean Mixed
  Food Club Brand - Pitted (Large, Medium)
  Great Value Brand (Wal-Mart) -
    Large Pitted Ripe
    Medium Pitted Ripe
    Minced Pimento Stuffed (Manzanilla, Queen)
  Hannaford Brand -
    Pitted (Extra Large, Large, Medium, Small)
    Sliced (Ripe, Salad)
    Stuffed (Manzanilla, Queen)

Hy-Vee -
  Chopped Ripe
  Manzanilla Olives
  Medium Ripe Black
  Queen
  Ripe Black (Jumbo, Large)
  Sliced (Ripe Black, Salad)
Meijer Brand - Manzanilla Stuffed (Placed, Thrown, Tree), Queen
  (Stuffed Placed, Whole Thrown), Ripe (Large, Medium, Pitted
  Jumbo, Pitted Small, Sliced), Salad, Salad Sliced
Midwest Country Fare -
  Large Ripe Black
  Sliced Ripe Black
Peloponnese - Kalamata Olives
Publix - Colossal, Green, Large, Ripe, Small
Safeway Brand - Black Olives, Manzanilla
Santa Barbara Olive Co. - Garlic Stuffed
Spartan Brand - Pitted Olives (Jumbo, Large, Medium, Sliced, Small)
Tassos -
  Blonde Olives In Extra Virgin Olive Oil & Red Wine Vinegar
  Evian Olives In Sea Salt Brine
  Greek Black Olives In Extra Virgin Olive Oil & Red Wine Vinegar
  Kalamata In Tassos Extra Virgin Olive Oil & Red Wine Vinegar
  Stuffed Almond In Sea Salt Brine
Wegmans Brand -
  Greek Mix
  Kalamata (Pitted, Whole)
  Ripe (Pitted Colossal, Pitted Extra Large, Pitted Medium, Sliced)
  Spanish (Manzanilla, Queen, Salad)
  Stuffed w/ (Almonds, Garlic, Red Peppers)
Winn Dixie - Green (All Varieties), Ripe (All Varieties)

O

Onions... *All **Fresh** Onions Are **Gluten/Casein/Soy Free***
  Albertsons - Frozen
  Birds Eye - All Plain Frozen Onions
  Lowes Foods Brand - Frozen Diced
  Meijer Brand - Frozen Chopped
  Publix - Frozen (Chopped, Diced)
  Trader Joe's - All Plain Frozen Onions
  Wegmans Brand - Whole Onions In Brine
  Winn Dixie - Frozen Pearl Onions
Orange Juice... see **Drinks/Juice**
Oranges... *All **Fresh** Oranges Are **Gluten/Casein/Soy Free***
  Sunkist
Oyster Sauce
  Panda Brand -
    Green Label Oyster Flavored Sauce
    Lo Mein Oyster Flavored Sauce
  Wok Mei - All Natural Oyster Flavored Sauce
Oysters... *All **Fresh** Seafood Is **Gluten/Casein/Soy Free**
    (Non-Marinated, Unseasoned)*
  Bumble Bee - Smoked, Whole
  Chicken Of The Sea -
    Smoked (In Oil, In Water)
    Whole
  Crown Prince -
    Smoked In (Cottonseed Oil, Pure Olive Oil)
    Whole Boiled
  Great Value Brand (Wal-Mart) - Canned Smoked Oysters
  Ocean Prince -
    Fancy Whole Smoked In Cottonseed Oil
    Whole Boiled

P P

Pancakes/Pancake Mix & Waffles/Waffle Mix

1-2-3 Gluten Free▲ - Allie's Awesome Buckwheat Pancakes●

Arrowhead Mills - Gluten Free Pancake & Waffle Mix

Authentic Foods▲ - Pancake & Baking Mix

Bob's Red Mill▲ - Gluten Free Pancake Mix

Breads From Anna▲ - Pancake & Muffin Mix (Apple, Cranberry, Maple)

Cherrybrook Kitchen - Gluten Free Pancake Mix *(Box Must Say Gluten-Free)*

Gluten Free Sensations - Pancake & Waffle Mix

Gluten-Free Creations▲ - Buckwheat Pancake Mix●, Mighty Mesquite Pancake Mix●

Gluten-Free Essentials▲ - Pancake & Waffle Mix

Grandma Ferdon's▲ - Pancake/Waffle Mix

Hodgson Mill▲ - Gluten Free Pancake & Waffle Mix

Hol Grain - Pancake & Waffle Mix

Laurel's Sweet Treats▲ - Bulk Pancake Mix, Pancake & Waffle Mix

Manischewitz - Pancake Mix (Potato, Sweetened Potato)

Mixes From The Heartland ▲ - Pancake Mix (Apple Cinnamon●, Cornmeal●, Country●)

Namaste Foods▲ - Waffle & Pancake Mix

Only Oats - Whole Oat Pancake Mix●

Orgran▲ - Apple & Cinnamon Pancake Mix, Buckwheat Pancake Mix, Plain Pancake Mix w/Sorghum

Pamela's Products ▲ - Baking & Pancake Mix●

Really Good Foods Company - Classic Pancake Mix

Ruby Range - Southwest Pancakes Gluten Free Baking Mix●

Papaya... *All Fresh Papaya Is **Gluten/Casein/Soy Free***

Native Forest - Organic Papaya Chunks

Woodstock Farms - Organic Frozen Papaya Chunks

Pappadums
  Patak's - Pappadums (Black Peppercorn, Garlic, Plain)
  Sharwood's - Indian Puppodums (Plain)
Paprika... see Seasonings
Parmesan Cheese... see Cheese
Pasta
  Allegaroo▲ - Chili Mac, Spaghetti, Spyglass Noodles
  Ancient Harvest Quinoa - Elbows, Garden Pagodas, Linguine, Rotelle, Shells, Spaghetti, Veggie Curls
  Annie Chun's - Rice Noodles (Maifun, Pad Thai)
  Aproten - Fettuccine, Fusilli, Penne, Rigatini, Spaghetti, Tagliatelle
  Bi-Aglut - Fusilli, Maccheroncini, Penne, Spaghetti
  Conte's Pasta - Gnocchi, Potato Onion Pierogies
  Cornito - Elbow Macaroni, Mystic Flames Noodles, Rainbow Rotini, Rigatoni, Rotini, Sea Waves, Spaghetti
  DeBoles -
    Corn Pasta (Elbow Style, Spaghetti)
    Gluten Free Rice (Angel Hair & Golden Flax, Spirals & Golden Flax)
    Gluten Free Whole Grain (Penne, Spaghetti)
    Rice Pasta (Angel Hair, Fettuccini, Lasagna, Penne, Spaghetti, Spirals)
  Eden Organic - Bifun, Kuzu, Mung Bean
  Ener-G▲ - White Rice (Lasagna, Macaroni, Small Shells, Spaghetti, Vermicelli)
  Gillian's Foods▲ - Fettuccini, Fusilli, Penne, Spaghetti
  Glutano▲ - Fusilli, Penne, Spaghetti
  Glutino▲ - Brown Rice (Fusilli, Macaroni, Penne, Spaghetti)
  Grandma Ferdon's▲ - Brown Rice (Chow Mein Noodles, Elbows, Fettuccini, Lasagna, Spaghetti)
  Hodgson Mill▲ - Gluten Free Brown Rice (Angel Hair Pasta, Elbows, Linguine, Penne, Spaghetti)

P

Lundberg▲ - Organic Brown Rice Pasta (Elbow, Penne, Rotini, Spaghetti)

Mrs. Leeper's - Corn Pasta (Elbows, Rotelli, Spaghetti, Vegetable Radiatore), Rice Pasta (Alphabets, Elbows, Kids Shapes, Penne, Spaghetti, Vegetable Twists)

Namaste Foods▲ - Pasta Meals (Pasta Pisavera, Say Cheez, Taco)

Notta Pasta - Fettuccine, Linguine, Spaghetti

Orgran▲ -

    Buckwheat Spirals

    Buontempo Rice Pasta (Penne, Shells, Spirals)

    Canned (Alternative Grain Spaghetti, Spaghetti In Tomato Sauce, Spirals In Tomato Sauce)

    Corn & Spinach Rigati

    Corn & Vegetable Pasta Shells

    Corn Pasta Spirals

    Essential Fibre (Penne, Spirals)

    Garlic & Parsley Rice Pasta Shells

    Italian Style Spaghetti

    Pasta & Sauce (Tomato Basil)

    Pasta Ready Meals (Tomato & Basil, Vegetable Bolognese)

    Rice & Corn (Herb Pasta, Macaroni, Mini Lasagne Sheets, Penne, Risoni Garlic Herb, Spaghetti, Spirals, Tortelli, Vegetable Animal Shapes, Vegetable Corkscrews)

    Rice & Millet Spirals

    Rice Pasta Spirals

    Super Grains Multigrain Pasta w/(Amaranth, Quinoa)

    Tomato & Basil Corn Pasta

    Vegetable Rice (Penne, Spirals)

Pastariso▲ - Organic Brown Rice (Angel Hair, Elbows, Fettuccine, Lasagna, Linguine, Penne, Rotini, Spaghetti, Vermicelli), Spinach Spaghetti, Vegetable Rotini

Pastato▲ - Elbows, Shells, Spaghetti

P

Rizopia -

> Brown Rice (Elbows, Fettuccine, Fusilli, Lasagne, Penne, Shells, Spaghetti, Spirals)

> Organic Brown Rice (Elbows, Fantasia, Fettuccine, Fusilli, Penne, Spaghetti)

> Organic Wild Rice (Elbows, Fusilli, Penne, Radiatore, Shells, Spaghetti)

> Spinach Brown Rice Spaghetti

> Vegetable Brown Rice Fusilli

> White Rice Spaghetti

Sam Mills▲ - Corn Pasta (Conchiliette, Cornetti Rigati, Fusilli, Lasagna, Penne Rigate, Rigatoni, Tubetti Rigati)

Schar▲ - Anellini, Fusilli, Multigrain Penne Rigate, Penne, Spaghetti, Tagliatelle

Seitenbacher - Gourmet Noodles Gluten Free Golden Ribbon, Gluten Free Rigatoni

Tinkyada▲ -

> Brown Rice (Elbows, Fettuccini, Fusilli, Grand Shells, Lasagne, Little Dreams, Penne, Shells, Spaghetti, Spirals)

> Organic Brown Rice (Elbows, Lasagne, Penne, Spaghetti, Spirals)

> Spinach Brown Rice Spaghetti

> Vegetable Brown Rice Spirals

> White Rice Spaghetti

Westbrae - Corn Angel Hair Pasta

Pasta Sauce... see Sauces

Pastrami

> **Dietz & Watson -** Pastrami Brisket, Spiced Beef Pastrami

> **Hormel -** Deli Sliced Cooked

> **Jennie-O Turkey Store -** Refrigerated Dark Turkey Pastrami

> **Perdue -** Deli Dark Turkey Pastrami Hickory Smoked

> **Wellshire Farms -** Pastrami (Brisket, Round, Sliced Beef)

P Pastry Mix

    Orgran▲ - All Purpose

Pate

    Kootenay Kitchen - Vege Pate (Curry, Herb, Jalapeno)

    Tartex - Pate (Herb Meadow, Mushroom, Original)

Pea Pods... see also Peas... *All Fresh Pea Pods Are Gluten/Casein/Soy Free*

    Meijer Brand - Frozen (Chinese)

Peaches... *All Fresh Peaches Are Gluten/Casein/Soy Free*

    Albertsons - All Canned Peaches, Frozen

    Cascadian Farm - Organic Frozen Sliced Peaches

    Del Monte -

        Canned/Jarred Fruit (All Varieties)

        Fruit Snack Cups (Metal, Plastic)

    Dole - All Fruits (Bowls, Canned, Dried, Frozen, Jars) *(Except Real Fruit Bites)*

    Food Club Brand - Fruit Cups Diced Peaches, Frozen Peaches, Halves In Heavy Syrup, Sliced In Heavy Syrup, Sliced Lite

    Hannaford Brand -

        Extra Light Syrup (Halves, Sliced)

        No Sugar Added Sliced

        Sliced In Heavy Syrup

    Home Harvest Brand - Yellow Cling Peaches (In Light Syrup, Sliced)

    Hy-Vee -

        Diced

        Diced Fruit Cups

        Halves

        Lite (Diced, Halves, Slices)

        Peaches In Strawberry Gel

        Slices

P

Great Value Brand (Wal-Mart) -
  Cling Peach Halves In Light Syrup
  No Sugar Added Yellow Cling Peach Halves In Pear Juice From
    Concentrate & Water
Kroger Brand - Fruit (Canned, Cups)
Laura Lynn - Canned
Lowes Foods Brand - Slices (In Heavy Syrup, In Juice)
Meijer Brand -
  Cling Halves (In Heavy Syrup, In Juice Lite, In Pear Juice Lite)
  Cling Sliced (In Heavy Syrup, In Juice, In Pear Juice Lite)
  Frozen (Organic, Sliced)
  Pallet Mod
  Yellow Sliced in Heavy Syrup
Midwest Country Fare - Lite Peaches (Halves, Slices), Slices
Publix -
  Canned (Lite Yellow Cling Peaches in Pear Juice Halves & Slices,
    Yellow Cling Peaches In Heavy Syrup Halves & Slices)
  Frozen Sliced Peaches
S&W - All Plain Canned/Jarred Fruits
Safeway Brand - Canned Peaches (Halves, Halves Lite, Sliced, Sliced
  Lite), Frozen
Spartan Brand - Cling Halves (Heavy Syrup, Regular), Diced
  (Heavy Syrup, Light Syrup), Frozen, Lite Cling Halves, Sliced
  Cling Peaches In Pear, Yellow Cling Sliced
Thrifty Maid - Yellow Cling Halves & Slices
Wegmans Brand - Sliced Yellow Cling (In Heavy Syrup, Raspberry)
Winn Dixie -
  Frozen Sliced
  Yellow Cling Halves & Slices (Heavy Syrup, Light Syrup)
Woodstock Farms - Organic Frozen Peach Slices

P Peanut Butter... (includes Nut Butters)
    Arrowhead Mills -
        Almond Butter (Creamy, Crunchy)
        Cashew Butter (Creamy, Crunchy)
        Organic Valencia Peanut Butter (Creamy, Crunchy)
        Valencia Peanut Butter (Creamy, Crunchy)
    Bee's Knees - All Varieties
    Earth Balance -
        Creamy Natural Almond Butter
        Natural Peanut Butter (Creamy, Crunchy)
    Hannaford Brand - Creamy, Crunchy
    MaraNatha -
        Natural Creamy (No Stir, With Salt)
        Natural Crunchy (No Stir, With Salt)
        Organic Creamy (No Salt, No Stir, With Salt)
        Organic Crunchy (No Salt, No Stir, With Salt)
        Organic No Stir Calcium
    Midwest Country Fare - Creamy, Crunchy
    Peanut Butter & Co. - All Varieties *(EXCEPT Dark Chocolate & White Chocolate Wonderful)*
    Publix - All Natural (Creamy, Crunchy)
    Santa Cruz -
        Organic Dark Roasted (Creamy, Crunchy)
        Organic Light Roasted (Creamy, Crunchy)
    Skippy - Natural (Creamy, Super Chunk)
    Smart Balance - Omega (Chunky, Creamy)
    Smucker's -
        Goober (Grape, Strawberry)
        Natural (Chunky, Creamy, Honey, No Salt Added Creamy, Reduced Fat)
    Walden Farms - Creamy Peanut Spread (Sugar Free)

P

Wegmans Brand -
> Natural Peanut Butter (Creamy, Crunchy)
> Organic Natural Peanut Butter w/Peanut Skins (Creamy, Crunchy)
> Organic PB No Stir (Creamy, Crunchy)

Woodstock Farms -
> Non Organic Nut Butters
>> Almond Butter (Crunchy Unsalted, Smooth Unsalted)
>> Cashew Butter Unsalted
>> Raw Almond
>> Tahini Unsalted
> Organic Nut Butters
>> Almond Butter (Crunchy Unsalted, Smooth Unsalted)
>> Classic Peanut Butter (Crunchy Salted, Smooth Salted)
>> Easy Spread Peanut Butter (Crunchy (Salted, Unsalted), Smooth (Salted, Unsalted))
>> Peanut Butter (Crunchy (Salted, Unsalted), Smooth (Salted, Unsalted))
>> Raw Almond
>> Tahini Unsalted

Peanut Sauce
> **A Taste Of Thai -** Peanut Satay Sauce
> **Mr. Spice Organic -** Thai Peanut Sauce & Marinade

Peanuts... see Nuts

Pears... *All Fresh Pears Are Gluten/Casein/Soy Free*
> **Albertsons -** Canned
> **Del Monte -**
>> Canned/Jarred Fruit (All Varieties)
>> Fruit Snack Cups (All Varieties)
> **Dole -** All Fruits (Bowls, Canned, Dried, Frozen, Jars) *(Except Real Fruit Bites)*

P **Food Club Brand** - Fruit Cups (Diced Pears), Sliced

Full Circle - Organic (Halves In Juice, Sliced In Juice)

Great Value Brand (Wal-Mart) -

Bartlett Pear Halves In Heavy Syrup

Bartlett Sliced Pears In Heavy Syrup

No Sugar Added Bartlett (Chunky Mixed Fruits, Fruit Cocktail, Pear Halves) In Pear Juice From Concentrate & Water

Hannaford Brand - Diced In Light Syrup, Extra Light Syrup (Halves, Sliced) No Sugar Added (Halves, Sliced)

Home Harvest Brand - Whole Pears (In Light Syrup, Regular)

Hy-Vee - Bartlett Pears (Halves, Sliced), Diced Bartlett Pears Cups, Lite Pears

Kroger Brand - Fruit (Canned, Cups)

Laura Lynn - Canned Pears

Lowes Foods Brand - Halves (In Heavy Syrup, In Juice)

Meijer Brand - Halves (Heavy Syrup, In Juice, In Juice Lite, Lite), Slices (Heavy Syrup, In Juice Lite)

Midwest Country Fare - Bartlett Pear Halves In Light Syrup

Native Forest - Organic Sliced Asian Pears

Publix - Canned (Bartlett Pears In Heavy Syrup (Halves, Slices), Lite Bartlett Pear Halves In Pear Juice)

S&W - All Plain Canned/Jarred Fruits

Safeway Brand - Canned Pears (Halves, Halves Lite, Sliced, Sliced Lite)

Spartan Brand - Halves (Heavy Syrup, Lite Syrup), Slices (Heavy Syrup, In Juice)

Stop & Shop Brand - Bartlett Pear Halves (Heavy Syrup, Light Syrup, Pear Juice, Splenda)

Thrifty Maid - Bartlett Halves & Slices

Wegmans Brand - Halves (Heavy Syrup, Regular), Sliced (Heavy Syrup, Regular)

Winn Dixie - Bartlett Halves & Slices (Heavy Syrup, Light Syrup)

P

Peas... *All **Fresh** Peas Are **Gluten/Casein/Soy Free***

Albertsons - Canned, Frozen

Birds Eye - All Plain Frozen Peas

C & W - All Plain Frozen Peas

Cascadian Farms - Organic Frozen (Garden Peas, Peas & Carrots, Peas & Pearl Onions, Purely Steam Petite Sweet Peas, Sugar Snap Peas, Sweet Peas)

Del Monte - All Plain Canned Peas

Food Club Brand - Canned Sweet, Frozen (Green Peas, Peas & Carrots, Sugar Snap)

Freshlike - Select (Petite Sweet Peas, Sweet Peas & Tiny Onions), Sweet Peas & Carrots, Tender Garden

Full Circle - Organic Frozen Peas, Organic Sweet Peas

Grand Selections - Frozen (Petite Green, Sugar Snap)

Great Value Brand (Wal-Mart) - Canned (Blackeye Peas, No Salt Added Sweet Peas, Sweet Peas), Frozen Sweet Peas, Microwaveable Plastic Cups Sweet Peas

Green Giant -

Canned Sweet Peas

Frozen

Simply Steam (Baby Sweet Peas, Sugar Snap Peas)

Sweet Peas

Halstead Acres - Blackeye Peas

Hannaford Brand - No Salt, Petite, Sweet

Health Market Organic - Sweet

Home Harvest Brand - Canned Sweet, Frozen

Hy-Vee - Black Eyed, Dry Green Split, Frozen Sweet, Steam In A Bag Frozen Peas, Sweet

Kroger Brand - All Plain Peas (Canned, Frozen)

Laura Lynn - Canned Blackeye Peas, Sweet Peas, Tiny June Peas

Lowes Foods Brand - Black Eyed, Frozen (Crowder, Field Peas, Green, Peas, Peas & Carrots, Tiny Green), Split Green Peas

P Meijer Brand -

Canned (Blackeye, Peas & Sliced Carrots, Small, Sweet, Sweet No Salt, Sweet Organic)

Frozen Peas (Green, Green Petite, Organic Green, Peas & Sliced Carrots)

Midwest Country Fare - Frozen Green, Sweet

O Organics - Frozen Sweet Peas

Pictsweet - All Plain Frozen Peas

Publix -

Canned Sweet Peas (No Salt Added, Regular, Small)

Frozen (Green, Field Peas w/Snap, Original, Peas & Carrots, Petite)

Publix GreenWise Market - Organic Canned Sweet Peas

S&W - All Canned Plain Peas

Safeway Select - Frozen (Blackeyed, Green, Peas & Carrots, Petite), Steam In Bag (Pod, Peas & Onions, Petite Green)

Spartan Brand - Canned (Green, Sweet), Dried (Blackeyed, Green Split), Frozen (Blackeyed, Crowder, Peas, Peas & Carrots, Peas w/Snaps, Petite, Sugar Snap, w/Snaps)

Trader Joe's - All Plain Frozen Peas

Wegmans Brand - Blackeye, Regular, Small Sweet, Sugar Snap Frozen, Sweet (No Salt Added, Regular), Sweet Petite Frozen, w/Pearl Onions Frozen

Winn Dixie -

Canned Green Peas (Large, Medium, No Salt Added, Small, Tiny)

Frozen (Crowder, Field w/Snaps, Green, Organic Green, Peas & Carrots, Petite Green, Purple Hull)

Woodstock Farms - Organic Frozen (Green Peas, Peas & Carrots, Petite Peas, Sugar Snap)

Wylwood - Blackeye Peas

Pepper Rings

Meijer Brand - Banana Pepper Rings (Hot, Mild)

Publix - Banana Pepper Rings (Mild)

Spartan Brand - Pepper Rings (Mild, Hot)

Vlasic -
- Hot Chili Peppers
- Hot Pepper Rings
- Mild Pepper Rings
- Mild Pepperoncini Peppers
- Sweet Roasted Pepper Strips

Pepper Sauce... see Chili Sauce and/or Hot Sauce

Pepperoni... see Sausage

Peppers... *All Fresh Peppers Are Gluten/Casein/Soy Free*

Albertsons - Frozen Diced Green

B&G -
- Giardiniera
- Hot Cherry Peppers (Red & Green, Regular)
- Hot Chopped Peppers (Regular, Roasted)
- Hot Jalapenos (Cherry, Chopped)
- Hot Pepper Rings
- Pepperoncini
- Roasted (w/Balsamic Vinegar, w/Oregano & Garlic)
- Sweet (Cherry Peppers, Fried)

Birds Eye - All Plain Frozen Peppers

Di Lusso - Roasted Red

Hannaford Brand - Whole Pepperoncini

Hy-Vee - Diced Green Chilies, Green Salad Pepperoncini, Hot Banana Peppers, Mild Banana Peppers, Salad Peppers, Sliced Hot Jalapenos, Whole Green Chilies

La Victoria - Diced Jalapenos, Nacho Jalapenos Sliced

Meijer Brand - Frozen Green Peppers Chopped

Peloponnese - Rainbow Peppers, Roasted Florida Sweet Pepper Strips, Whole Roasted Florida Sweet Peppers

Publix - Frozen Green Peppers (Diced)

Safeway Select - Fire Roasted, Frozen Pepper Strips

P   **Spartan Brand** - Jalapeno Peppers

Stop & Shop Brand - Chopped Green

Trappey - Jalapeno (Sliced, Whole)

Vlasic -

Hot Chili Peppers

Hot Pepper Rings

Mild Pepper Rings

Mild Pepperoncini Peppers

Sweet Roasted Pepper Strips

Wegmans Brand - Clean And Cut Peppers & Onions (Diced, Sliced), Pepper & Onions Mix, Roasted Red Peppers Whole

Winn Dixie - Pepperoncini, Sliced Banana Peppers (Hot, Mild)

Woodstock Farms - Organic Frozen Tri Colored Peppers

Picante Sauce

Albertsons - Medium, Mild

Chi-Chi's - Smooth & Spicy

Hy-Vee - Hot, Medium, Mild

Winn Dixie - Medium, Mild

Pickled Beets... see Beets

Pickles

Albertsons - All Varieties

B&G -

Bread & Butter

Hamburger Dill

Kosher Dill (Baby Gherkins, Gherkins, Original)

Midget Gherkins

NY Deli Dill

Pickle In A Pouch

Sour

Sweet (Gherkins, Mixed, Mixed Pickles)

Tiny Treats

Unsalted (Bread & Butter, Kosher Dill)

Zesty Dill

Boar's Head - All Varieties

Hannaford Brand - Bread & Butter Chips, Bread & Butter Sandwich Slices, Kosher Baby Dills, Kosher Dill (Regular, Sandwich Slices, Spears), Kosher Petite, Polish Dill Spears, Sour Dill, Spear & Chips Sugar Free Bread & Butter, Sugar Free Sweet Gherkin, Sweet Gherkins (Midgets, Mixed Chips)

Hy-Vee -

Bread & Butter (Sandwich Slices, Sweet Chunk Pickles, Sweet Slices)

Dill (Kosher Sandwich Slices, Relish)

Fresh Pack Kosher Baby Dills

Hamburger Dill Slices

Kosher (Baby Dills, Cocktail Dills, Dill Pickles, Dill Spears)

Polish Dill (Pickles, Spears)

Refrigerated Kosher Dill (Halves, Sandwich Slices, Spears, Whole Pickles)

Special Recipe (Baby Dills, Bread & Butter Slices, Hot & Spicy Zingers, Hot & Sweet Zinger Chunks, Jalapeno Baby Dills, Sweet Garden Crunch)

Meijer Brand - Bread & Butter (Chips (Regular, Sugar Free), Sandwich Slice), Dill (Hamburger, Kosher (Whole), Polish, Sandwich Slice (Polish), Spears (Polish, Zesty)), Kosher (Baby Dill, Sandwich Slices, Whole), Sweet (Gherkin, Midgets, Sugar Free, Whole)

Midwest Country Fare - Dill, Hamburger Dill Pickle Slices, Kosher Dill, Whole Sweet

Mrs. Renfro's - Green Tomato Pickles

Publix - All Varieties

Safeway Brand - All Varieties

P   Spartan Brand -
>>> Bread & Butter Pickle (Slices)
>>> Hamburger Dill Slices
>>> Kosher Dill (Baby, Slices, Spears, Whole)
>>> Plain Baby Dills
>>> Polish Dill (Regular, Spears)
>>> Sweet (Gherkin Whole, Regular, Slices)

Vlasic -
>>> Baby Kosher (Dills, Spears)
>>> Bread & Butter
>>> Hamburger Dill Chips
>>> Sweet & Crunchy Sweet
>>> Sweet (Gherkins, Sweet Midgets)
>>> Zesty (Dill, Garlic)

Wegmans Brand -
>>> Hamburger Dill Slices
>>> Kosher Dill (Baby Dills, Slices, Spears, Spears Reduced Sodium, Whole)
>>> Polish Dill (Spears, Whole)
>>> Refrigerated Kosher Dills (Halves, Mini, Sandwich Slices, Spears, Whole)

Winn Dixie - Dill (All Varieties), Sweet Pickles (All Varieties), Sweet Relish

Woodstock Farms - Organic (Kosher Dill (Baby, Sliced, Whole), Sweet Bread & Butter)

Pie

Amy's - Organic Mexican Tamale Pie

Mixes From The Heartland▲ - Pie Mix (Impossible Coconut●, Impossible Pumpkin●)

Pie Crust/Pie Crust Mix

Authentic Foods▲ - Pie Crust Mix

Breads From Anna▲ - Piecrust Mix

P

El Peto▲ - Perfect Pie Crust Mix

Hodgson Mill▲ - GF Pizza Crust Mix

Mixes From The Heartland▲ - Pie Crust Mix●

Namaste Foods▲ - Biscuits Piecrust & More Mix

Pie Filling

Comstock - Apple, Blueberry, Cherry, Peach

Fischer & Wieser - Fredericksburg Golden Peach, Harvest Apple & Brandy

Great Value Brand (Wal-Mart) - No Sugar Added (Apple, Cherry)

Hy-Vee - More Fruit Pie Filling/Topping (Apple, Cherry)

Jell-O -

  Regular Cook & Serve

    Banana Cream

    Chocolate (Fudge, Regular)

    Coconut Cream

    Vanilla

  Regular Instant Pudding & Pie Filling

    Banana Cream

    Chocolate (Fudge, Regular)

    Coconut Cream

    Devil's Food

    French Vanilla

    Lemon

    Pistachio

    Pumpkin Spice

    Vanilla

    White Chocolate

  Sugar Free Fat Free Cook & Serve

    Chocolate

    Vanilla

P **Lucky Leaf** - Blueberry, Cherry, Chocolate Crème, Coconut Crème, Dark Sweet Cherry, Key Lime Pie Crème, Lemon, Lemon Crème, Lite (Apple, Cherry), Peach, Premium (Apple, Blackberry, Blueberry, Cherry, Red Raspberry), Strawberry

Meijer Brand - 100% Pure Pumpkin, Apple, Blueberry, Cherry, Cherry Lite, Peach

Midwest Country Fare - Apple, Cherry

Musselman's - Apple, Cherries Jubilee, Cherry, Peach

Spartan Brand - Apple, Blueberry, Cherry (Lite, Regular)

Winn Dixie - Apple, Blueberry, Cherry

Pilaf

Trader Joe's - Thai Style Lime, Wild & Basmati Rice

Pimentos

Meijer Brand - Pieces, Sliced

Winn Dixie - Sliced

Pineapple... *All **Fresh** Pineapple Is **Gluten/Casein/Soy Free***

Albertsons - All Varieties

Del Monte -

Canned/Jarred Fruit (All Varieties)

Fruit Snack Cups (Metal, Plastic)

Dole - All Fruits (Bowls, Canned, Dried, Frozen, Jars) *(Except Real Fruit Bites)*

Food Club Brand - Chunks, Crushed, Sliced, Tidbits

Great Value Brand (Wal-Mart) - Chunks, Pineapple In Unsweetened Pineapple Juice (Crushed, Slices), Tidbits

Hannaford Brand - Chunks, Crushed, No Sugar Added Sliced

Hy-Vee - Chunk, Crushed, In Lime Gel, Sliced, Tidbit Fruit Cup

Kroger Brand - Fruit (Canned, Cups)

Laura Lynn - Canned

Lowes Foods Brand - Chunks In Juice, Crushed In Juice, Sliced In Juice

Meijer Brand - Chunks (Heavy Syrup, In Juice), Crushed (Heavy Syrup, In Juice), Frozen Chunks, Sliced In (Heavy Syrup, Juice)

Midwest Country Fare - Chunks, Crushed, Slices, Tidbits

Native Forest - Organic (Chunks, Crushed, Slices)

Publix - Canned (All Varieties)

Safeway Brand - Chunks, Crushed, Sliced

Spartan Brand - Chunks, Crushed, Tidbits

Stop & Shop Brand - Frozen Pineapple

Wegmans Brand - Chunk, Crushed, Sliced (In Heavy Syrup, Regular), Tidbits

Winn Dixie - Chunks, Crushed, Sliced, Tidbits

Pistachio Nuts... see Nuts

Pizza Crust/Pizza Mix

Bob's Red Mill▲ - GF Pizza Crust Mix

Chebe▲ - Pizza Mix●

Ener-G▲ - Rice Pizza Shell (6", 10"), Yeast Free Rice Pizza Shell (6", 10")

Food-Tek Fast & Fresh - Dairy Free Minute Pizza Crust Mix

Foods By George▲ - Pizza Crusts

Gluten Free & Fabulous▲ - Pizza Crust●

Gluten-Free Creations▲ - Italian Seasoned Crust●, Simply Pizza Crust●, Whole Grain Crust●

Glutino▲ - Premium Pizza Crust

Kinnikinnick▲ - Pizza Crust (7", 10"), Pizza Crust Mix

Namaste Foods▲ - Pizza Crust Mix

Orgran▲ - Pizza & Pastry Multi Mix

Rose's Bakery▲ - All Varieties●

Pizza Sauce... see also Sauces

Contadina

El Peto▲ - Pre Baked (Basil, Millet, White)

Eden Organic - Organic Pizza Pasta Sauce

Meijer Brand

Muir Glen - Organic

Sauces 'N Love - Marinara Fresh

P Plum Sauce

    Sharwood's

    Winn Dixie

    Wok Mei - All Natural Plum Sauce

Plums... *All Fresh Plums Are Gluten/Casein/Soy Free*

    Hy-Vee - Purple Plums

    Stop & Shop Brand - Whole Plums In Heavy Syrup

    Winn Dixie - Canned Whole Plums

Polenta

    Bob's Red Mill▲ - Gluten Free Corn Grits/Polenta

    Food Merchants Brand - Ready Made Organic (Ancient Harvest Quinoa, Basil & Garlic, Chili Cilantro, Mushroom & Onion, Sun Dried Tomato, Traditional)

Pomegranate... *All Fresh Pomegranate Is Gluten/Casein/Soy Free*

    Woodstock Farms - Organic Frozen Pomegranate Kernels

Pop... see Soda Pop/Carbonated Beverages

Popcorn

    Eden Organic - Organic Popping Kernels

    Farmer Steve's - Kernels, Organic Microwave

    Hannaford Brand - Kettle Corn, Natural, White Kernels, Yellow Kernels

    Home Harvest Brand - Kernels (White, Yellow)

    Hy-Vee - Kernels (White, Yellow)

    Jolly Time - Kernel Corn (American's Best, Organic Yellow, White, Yellow)

    Kroger Brand - Plain Popcorn Kernels

    Meijer Brand -

        Microwave (Kettle Sweet & Salty, Natural Lite)

        Regular (White, Yellow)

    Newman's Own - Regular (Raw Popcorn)

    Newman's Own Organics - Microwave Pop's Corn (No Butter No Salt 94% Fat Free)

    Pirate's Booty - Barbeque

Safeway Brand - Yellow Kernels

Skeete & Ike's - Organic Sea Salt

Wegmans Brand - Yellow Kernels

Pork... *All Fresh Meat Is Gluten/Casein/Soy Free (Non-Marinated, Unseasoned)*

Always Tender - Flavored Fresh Pork (Mojo Criollo)

Dietz & Watson - Barbecue Roast Of Pork, Boneless Pork Chops w/Natural Juices, Italian Style Roast Pork, Pork Cello Butt, Roast Sirloin Of Pork

Ejay's So. Smokehouse - All Natural Salt Pork

Homestyle Meals - Pork Baby Back Ribs w/BBQ Sauce, Shredded Pork In BBQ Sauce, Whole Bulk St. Louis Ribs w/BBQ Sauce

Jones Dairy Farm -

　All Natural

　　Hearty Pork Sausage Links●

　　Light Pork Sausage & Rice Links●

　　Little Link Pork Sausage●

　　Maple Sausage Patties●

　　Original Pork Roll Sausage●

　　Pork Sausage Patties●

　All Natural Golden Brown Cooked & Browned Sausage Patties (Maple Fully●, Mild Fully●)

　All Natural Golden Brown Light Fully Cooked & Browned Sausage & Rice Links●

Organic Prairie - Fresh Organic Pork (Chops 12 oz., Ground 1 lb., Loin, Loin Roast, Ribs)

Publix - Deli Pre Pack Sliced Lunch Meats (Spanish Style Pork)

Saz's - Barbecue Pork Meat Tub, Barbecued Baby Back Ribs

Wegmans Brand - Canned Pork & Beans In Tomato Sauce

Wellshire Farms - Whole Smoked Boneless Pork Loin

Potato Chips... see Chips

Potato Crisps... see Crisps

P Potatoes... *All **Fresh** Potatoes Are **Gluten/Casein/Soy Free***

Albertsons -
> Hash Browns (Country, Southern)
> Potatoes O'Brien

Alexia Foods -
> Crispy Potatoes w/Seasoned Salt Waffle Fries
> Julienne Fries Spicy Sweet Potato
> Julienne Fries Sweet Potato
> Julienne Fries w/Sea Salt Yukon Gold
> Olive Oil & Sea Salt Oven Fries
> Olive Oil Rosemary & Garlic Oven Fries
> Olive Oil Sun Dried Tomatoes & Pesto Oven Reds
> Organic (Classic Oven Crinkles, Oven Crinkles Onion & Garlic, Oven Crinkles Salt & Pepper, Seasoned Salt Hashed Browns, Yukon Gold Julienne Fries w/Sea Salt)
> Yukon Gold Potatoes w/Seasoned Salt Potato Nuggets

Cascadian Farm - Organic Frozen (Country Style Potatoes, Crinkle Cut French Fries, Hash Browns, Shoe String Fries, Spud Puppies, Straight Cut French Fries, Wedge Cut Oven Fries)

Funster - Natural Potato Letters (Original)

Great Value Brand (Wal-Mart) - Canned (Diced, Sliced, Whole New)

Hannaford Brand - Diced, Instant, Sliced, Whole

Hy-Vee -
> Canned (Sliced, Whole)
> Frozen (Country Style Hash Brown Potatoes, Potatoes O'Brien,)

Ian's - Alphatots

Manischewitz - Potato Mix (Homestyle Latke, Kugel, Mini Knish, Pancake, Sweetened Pancake)

Meijer Brand -
> Canned White (Sliced, Whole)
> Frozen French Fries (Quickie Crinkles)

P

Midwest Country Fare - Whole White Potatoes

Mixed From The Heartland ▲ - Texas Style Potatoes●

Ore-Ida -

  Frozen

    Hash Browns (Country Style, Original, Southern Style)

    Potatoes O'Brien

    Steam N' Mash (Cut Red, Cut Russet, Cut Sweet)

Publix -

  Canned (Sliced & Whole, White)

  Frozen (Southern Style Hash Browns)

S&W - All Plain Canned Potatoes

Safeway Brand -

  Hashbrowns Southern Style

  Instant Potatoes

Spartan Brand -

  Frozen (O'Brien Hash Browns, Shredded, Southern Style Hash Browns)

  Mashed Potatoes (Instant)

  White Sliced

  White Whole Sliced

Tasty Bite - Aloo Palak, Bombay, Mushroom Takatak

Wegmans Brand -

  Frozen Hash Browns (Country Style, O'Brien, Regular)

  White Potatoes (Peeled, Sliced)

Winn Dixie -

  Instant (Mashed Regular)

Woodstock Farms - Organic Frozen (Crinkle Cut Oven Fries, Shredded Hash Browns, Tastee Taters)

Preserves... see Jam/Jelly

P Pretzels

    Ener-G▲ - Wylde Pretzels (Poppy Seed, Regular, Sesame)

    Dutch Country - Soft Pretzel Mix

Protein

    Bob's Red Mill▲ - Hemp Protein Powder

    Living Harvest - Organic Hemp Protein Powder (Original, Vanilla Spice)

    MLO - Brown Rice Protein Powder

    Nutiva - Hemp Protein Shake (Amazon Acai, Berry Pomegranate, Chocolate), Protein Powder (Hemp, Hemp & Fiber)

    Ruth's - Organic Hemp Protein Powder (E3Live & Maca, Hemp Protein Power, Hemp w/Sprouted Flax & Maca

Protein Shakes... see Shakes... see also Protein

Prunes

    Great Value Brand (Wal-Mart) - Pitted Prunes

    Hannaford Brand - Pitted

    Meijer Brand - Pitted (Canister, Carton)

    Spartan Brand - Prunes Pitted

Pudding

    Hunt's - Pudding Snack Packs (Lemon, Lemon Meringue Pie)

    Jell-O -

        Regular Cook & Serve

            Banana Cream

            Chocolate (Fudge, Regular)

            Coconut Cream

            Vanilla

        Regular Instant Pudding & Pie Filling

            Banana Cream

            Chocolate (Fudge, Regular)

            Coconut Cream

            Devil's Food

P

Q

    French Vanilla
    Lemon
    Pistachio
    Pumpkin Spice
    Vanilla
    White Chocolate
  Sugar Free Fat Free Cook & Serve
    Chocolate
    Vanilla
Royal - All Instant Pudding (Regular, Sugar Free)
Spartan Brand - Cook & Serve (Chocolate, Vanilla)
Pumpkin... *All Fresh Pumpkin Is Gluten/Casein/Soy Free*
  Libby's - Canned (100% Pure Pumpkin, Easy Pumpkin Pie Mix)
  Meijer Brand - Canned
  Safeway Brand - Canned
  Wegmans Brand - Solid Pack
Puppodums
  Patak's - Pappadums (Black Peppercorn, Garlic, Plain)
  Sharwood's - Indian Puppodums (Plain)

Q

Quinoa
  Ancient Harvest Quinoa -
    Inca Red Quinoa
    Quinoa Flakes
    Quinoa Flour
    Quinoa Pasta (Elbows, Garden Pagodas, Linguine, Rotelle, Shells, Spaghetti, Veggie Curls)
    Traditional Quinoa Grain
  Arrowhead Mills - Quinoa

R R

Radishes... *All **Fresh** Radishes Are **Gluten/Casein/Soy Free***

Raisins

    Albertsons - Regular

    Great Value Brand (Wal-Mart) - California Sun Dried Raisins (100% Natural)

    Hannaford Brand

    Hy-Vee - California Sun Dried Raisins

    Meijer Brand - Canister, Seedless (Carton)

    Publix - Raisins

    Spartan Brand - Regular

    Sun-Maid - Raisins (Baking, Golden, Natural California, Regular), Zante Currants

    Wegmans Brand - Seedless

    Winn Dixie - Raisins (Organic, Regular)

    Woodstock Farms - Organic Raisins (Jumbo Thompson, Select Thompson), Raisins (Jumbo Flame)

Raspberries... *All **Fresh** Raspberries Are **Gluten/Casein/Soy Free***

    Cascadian Farm - Organic Frozen Raspberries

    Food Club Brand - Frozen Red Raspberries

    Full Circle - Organic Raspberries

    Hannaford Brand - In Syrup, Regular

    Hy-Vee - Frozen Red Raspberries

    Meijer Brand - Frozen (Organic, Regular), Red Individually Quick Frozen

    Publix - Frozen Raspberries

    Safeway Brand - Frozen Red Raspberries

    Spartan Brand - Frozen Red Raspberries

    Stop & Shop Brand - Raspberries, Raspberries In Syrup

    Wegmans Brand - Raspberries (Regular, w/Sugar)

    Winn Dixie - Frozen Red Raspberries

    Woodstock Farms - Organic Frozen Red Raspberries

R

Raspberry Vinaigrette... see Salad Dressing

Refried Beans... see Beans

Relish

   Albertsons - Sweet

   B&G - Dill, Emerald, Hamburger, Hot Dog, India, Piccalilli, Sweet, Unsalted

   Cascadian Farms

   Heinz - Hot Dog, India, Sweet

   Meijer Brand - Chipotle Flavored, Dill Relish, Sweet & Zesty, Sweet Relish (Sugar Free)

   Mrs. Renfro's - Corn, Hot Chow Chow, Hot Tomato, Mild Chow Chow, Mild Tomato

   Spartan Brand - Dill, Sweet

   Vlasic - Sweet

   Wegmans Brand - Dill, Hamburger, Sweet

   Woodstock Farms - Organic (Spicy Chipotle Sweet, Sweet Relish)

Ribs... *All Fresh Meat Is Gluten/Casein/Soy Free (Non-Marinated, Unseasoned)*

   Homestyle Meals - Pork Baby Back w/BBQ Sauce, Whole Bulk St. Louis Ribs w/BBQ Sauce

   Saz's - Barbecued Baby Back Ribs

Rice

   A Taste Of Thai - Jasmine Rice

   Albertsons - Boil In A Bag, Brown, White (Instant, Regular)

   Annie Chun's - Sprouted Brown Rice, Sticky White Rice

   Arrowhead Mills -

      Brown Basmati

      Long Grain Brown

      Short Brown

      White Basmati

   Dinty Moore - Microwave Meal (Rice w/Chicken)

R   Eden Organic -
    Organic Canned
        Curried Rice & Lentils
        Mexican Rice & Black Beans
        Moroccan Rice & Garbanzo Beans
        Rice & Cajun Small Red Beans
        Rice & Caribbean Black Beans
        Rice & Garbanzo Beans
        Rice & Kidney Beans
        Rice & Lentils
        Rice & Pinto Beans
        Spanish Rice & Pinto Beans

Fantastic World Foods - Arborio, Basmati, Jasmine

Food Club Brand - Instant Rice

Full Circle - Organic (Basmati Brown, Basmati White, Long Grain Brown, Long Grain White)

Gluten-Free Essentials▲ - Exotic Curry●, Italian Herb & Lemon●, Southwest Chipotle & Lime●

Go Go Rice - Organic Steamed Rice Bowls (Brown, White), Organic White Rice

Golden Star - Jasmine Rice

Great Value Brand (Wal-Mart) - Enriched Long Grain (Parboiled Rice, Rice Extra Fancy)

Hannaford Brand - Enriched Long Grain, Frozen Steam In Bag White Rice, Instant

Home Harvest Brand - 50% Broken Long Grain, Instant, Long Grain

Hormel -
    Compleats Microwaveable Meals
        Chicken & Rice
        Sante Fe Chicken & Rice

Hy-Vee -
  Boil In Bag Rice
  Enriched Extra Long Grain (Instant, Regular)
  Extra Long Grain
  Instant Brown
  Natural Long Grain Brown

Konriko -
  Original Brown Rice (Bag)
  Wild Pecan Rice (Box, Burlap Bag)

Kraft Minute Rice - Brown, White

Laura Lynn - Boil N' Bag, Instant, Long Grain White

Lotus Foods - Forbidden Black

Lowes Foods Brand - Boil N Bag, Instant (Brown, White), Long Grain

Lundberg▲ - All Varieties Of Plain Rice

Meijer Brand - Brown, Instant (Boil In Bag, Brown), Long Grain, Medium Grain

Midwest Country Fare - Pre Cooked Instant Rice

Minute Rice - Brown, White

Nishiki - Sushi Rice

O Organics - Long Grain (Brown, Thai Jasmine)

Publix -
  Long Grain (Brown, Enriched)
  Medium Grain White
  Pre Cooked Instant (Boil in Bag, Brown, White)

Royal - Basmati Rice

S&W - Natural Brown, White

Safeway Brand - Brown, Instant, Long Grain, Rice Pouch Gently Milled Bran Rice, White

Seeds Of Change -
  Amantani Whole Grain Blend Quinoa & Wild Rice

R **Shiloh Farms** - Brown Basmati Rice, Brown Rice, California Wild Rice

Spartan Brand - Instant (Boil In Bag, Brown Box, Regular Box), 4% Broken Long Grain

Stop & Shop Brand -
Instant Brown
Organic Long Grain (Brown & White)

Success - Boil In Bag (Jasmine Rice, Whole Grain Brown Rice, White Rice)

Tasty Bite - Basmati Rice & Spinach Dal

Thai Kitchen - Jasmine Rice

Thirsty Maid - Boil In A Bag

Trader Joe's - All Plain Grain Rice

Uncle Ben's -
Boil In Bag
Fast & Natural Instant Brown Rice
Instant Rice
Original Converted Brand Rice
Ready Rice (Original Long Grain Rice 8.8 oz & 14.8 oz)

Wegmans Brand -
Arborio Italian Style
Basmati
Boil In Bag
Enriched (Long, Long Grain White, Medium)
Instant (Brown, Regular)
Jasmine
Long Grain (Brown, Regular)
Medium Grain White

Rice Beverages

Amazake -
Almond Shake
Amazing Mango
Banana Appeal
Chocolate Almond

Cool Coconut

Gimme Green

Go Go Green

Go Hazelnuts

Oh So Original

Rice Nog

Tiger Chai

Vanilla Pecan Pie

Good Karma - Organic Ricemilk (Chocolate, Original, Vanilla)

Pacific Natural Foods - Low Fat Rice Beverage (Plain, Vanilla)

Rice Dream - Refrigerated & Shelf Stable Rice Beverages (All Varieties)

Wegmans Brand - Organic (Original, Vanilla)

Rice Cakes

Hannaford Brand - Fat Free Apple Cinnamon

Hy-Vee - Lightly Salted

Kroger Brand - Plain, Salted

Lundberg▲ -

Eco Farmed

Apple Cinnamon

Brown Rice (Lightly Salted, Salt Free)

Honey Nut

Toasted Sesame

Organic

Brown Rice (Lightly Salted, Salt Free)

Mochi Sweet

Rice w/Popcorn

Sweet Green Tea w/Lemon

Wild Rice

Spartan Brand - Salt Free

Stop & Shop Brand - Rice Cakes (Plain Salted, Plain Unsalted)

Rice Crackers... see Crackers

R Rice Cream
> Erewhon - Brown Rice Cream

S Rice Noodles... see Noodles... see also Pasta

Rice Syrup... see Syrup

Rice Vinegar... see Vinegar

Risotto
> Lundberg▲ - Organic (Florentine, Tuscan)

Roast Beef... see Beef

Rolls... see Bread

Rum... *All **Distilled** Alcohol Is **Gluten/Casein/Soy Free** [2]*

Rusks
> Glutino▲ - Gluten Free Rusks

Rutabaga... *All **Fresh** Rutabaga Is **Gluten/Casein/Soy Free***

S

Salad... *All **Fresh** Salad Is **Gluten/Casein/Soy Free***
> Mixes From The Heartland▲ - Pasta Salad (Corn N'Pasta●, Dilled●)
> Safeway Select - Mediterranean Salad

Salad Dressing
> Annie's Naturals -
>> Natural Dressings
>>> Lemon & Chive
>>> Lite Vinaigrette (Honey Mustard, Raspberry)
>>> Roasted Red Pepper Vinaigrette
>>> Tuscany Italian
>> Organic
>>> Balsamic Vinaigrette
>>> French
>>> Green Garlic

salad dressing

S

    Maple Ginger
    Oil & Vinegar
    Pomegranate Vinaigrette
    Roasted Garlic Vinaigrette

Bragg - Organic (Ginger & Sesame, Healthy Vinaigrette)

Briannas -
    Champagne Caper Vinaigrette
    Dijon Honey Mustard
    New American
    Rich Poppy Seed
    Santa Fe
    Vinaigrette (Blush Wine, Real French)
    Zesty French

Consorzio - Fat Free (Mango, Raspberry & Balsamic, Strawberry & Balsamic)

Drew's All Natural -
    Garlic Italian
    Green Olive & Caper
    Honey Dijon
    Poppy Seed
    Raspberry
    Roasted Garlic & Peppercorn
    Rosemary Balsamic
    Smoked Tomato

Emeril's - Caesar, Vinaigrette (Balsamic, House Herb, Italian, Raspberry Balsamic)

Fischer & Wieser - Original Roasted Raspberry Chipotle Vinaigrette

Follow Your Heart - Lemon Herb, Thousand Island

Girard's - Fat Free (Balsamic Vinaigrette, Raspberry)

Glutino▲ - French Herb Balsamic, Naturally Italian, Peppercorn Garlic

S

Henri's - Honey Mustard Fat Free

Ken's Steak House -

    Fat Free Dressings (Raspberry Pecan, Sun Dried Tomato)

    Healthy Options

        Balsamic Vinaigrette

    Lite Dressings Raspberry Walnut

Kraft -

    Dressing Made w/Extra Virgin Olive Oil (Italian Vinaigrette)

    Free (French)

    Light (Balsamic Vinaigrette)

Lily's Gourmet Dressings - Balsamic Vinaigrette

Litehouse -

    Pomegranate Blueberry Vinaigrette

    Poppyseed

    Red Wine Olive Oil Vinaigrette

    Spinach Salad

    Thousand Island

    Zesty Italian Vinaigrette

Maple Grove Farms Of Vermont -

    All Natural

        Blueberry Pomegranate

        Champagne Vinaigrette

        Ginger Pear

        Maple Fig

        Strawberry Balsamic

    Fat Free

        Cranberry Balsamic

        Greek

        Honey Dijon

        Lime Basil

        Vinaigrette (Balsamic, Raspberry)

salad dressing

S

    Organic (Dijon, Vinaigrette (Balsamic, Raspberry))

    Regular & Lite

       Balsamic Maple

       Sweet N' Sour

    Sugar Free (Italian Balsamic, Vinaigrette (Balsamic, Raspberry))

Marzetti - Fat Free Sweet & Sour

Pfeiffer - Italian Fat Free

Seeds Of Change - Balsamic Vinaigrette, French Tomato, Italian Herb, Roasted Red Pepper

Teresa's Select Recipes - Fat Free Honey Dijon

Walden Farms -

    Single Serve Packets (Creamy Bacon, Honey Dijon, Italian, Ranch, Thousand Island)

    Sugar Free No Carb

       Balsamic Vinaigrette

       Blue Cheese

       Coleslaw

       Creamy (Bacon, Italian)

       French

       Honey Dijon

       Italian

       Italian w/Sun Dried Tomato

       Ranch

       Raspberry Vinaigrette

       Russian

       Sweet Onion

       Thousand Island

       Zesty Italian

Wegmans Brand -

    Fat Free (Red Wine Vinegar, Roasted Red Pepper)

    Tarragon Vinaigrette

S   **Wild Thymes** - Salad Refresher (Black Currant, Mango, Meyer Lemon, Morello Cherry, Passion Fruit, Pomegranate, Raspberry, Tangerine), Vinaigrette (Fig Walnut, Mandarin Orange Basil, Mediterranean Balsamic, Parmesan Walnut Caesar, Raspberry Pear Balsamic, Roasted Apple Shallot, Tahitian Lime Ginger, Tuscan Tomato Basil)

Salami... see Sausage

Salmon... see also Fish... *All Fresh Fish Is Gluten/Casein/Soy Free (Non-Marinated, Unseasoned)*

  Chicken Of The Sea -

  Canned (Pink Salmon Chunk Style In Water, Pink Salmon Traditional Style)

  Pouch (Smoked Pacific Salmon)

  Crown Prince - Pink (Fancy Alaskan)

  Crown Prince Natural - Alaskan Pink, Alder Wood Smoked Alaskan Coho, Skinless & Boneless Pacific Pink

  Full Circle - All Natural Alaskan Sockeye Salmon Fillets

  Great Value Brand (Wal-Mart) - Canned Alaskan Pink Salmon

  Hannaford Brand - Canned Pink Salmon

  Hy-Vee - Frozen

  Publix - Coho Salmon Fillets, Sockeye Salmon Fillets

Salsa

  Albertsons - Chunky (Medium, Mild)

  Amy's - Organic (Black Bean & Corn, Fire Roasted Vegetable, Medium, Mild, Spicy Chipotle)

  Bone Suckin' - Salsa

  Bravos - Hot, Medium, Mild

  Chi-Chi's - Fiesta, Garden, Original

  Dei Fratelli - Black Bean 'N Corn Medium, Casera (Medium Hot, Mild), Chipotle Medium, Original (Medium, Mild)

  Drew's - Organic (Chipotle Lime Medium, Double Fire Roasted Medium, Hot, Medium, Mild)

  Eat Smart - Garden Style Sweet

salsa

S

Emeril's - Kicked Up Chunky Hot, Original Recipe Medium, Southwest Style Medium

Fischer & Wieser - Artichoke & Olive, Chipotle & Corn, Das Peach Haus Peach, Havana Mojito, Hot Habanero, Salsa A La Charra, Salsa Verde Ranchera, Sicilian Tomato Pesto

Frontera - Gourmet Mexican Salsa (Chipotle, Corn & Poblano, Double Roasted, Habanero, Jalapeno Cilantro, Mango Key Lime, Medium Chunky Tomato, Mild Chunky Tomato, Red Pepper & Garlic, Roasted Tomato, Tomatillo)

Grand Selections - Black Bean & Corn (Medium, Mild)

Green Mountain Gringo - All Varieties

Herdez - Salsa Casera Mild

Herr's - Chunky (Medium, Mild)

Hy-Vee - Thick & Chunky (Hot, Medium, Mild)

La Victoria -
Cilantro (Medium, Mild)
Hot
Jalapeno Extra Hot (Green, Red)
Salsa Ranchera
Salsa Ranchera Hot
Salsa Victoria Hot
Suprema (Medium, Mild)
Thick 'N Chunky (Hot, Medium, Mild)
Verde (Medium, Mild)

Meijer Brand -
Original (Hot, Medium, Mild)
Restaurant Style (Hot, Medium, Mild)
Santa Fe Style (Medium, Mild)
Thick & Chunky (Hot, Medium, Mild)

Miguel's - Black Bean & Corn, Chipotle, Medium, Mild, Roasted Garlic

S

Mrs. Renfro's - Black Bean, Chipotle Corn, Garlic, Green, Habanero, Hot, Mango Habanero, Medium, Mexican (Hot, Mild), Mild, Peach, Pineapple, Pomegranate, Raspberry Chipotle, Roasted, Tequila

Muir Glen - Organic (Medium, Medium Black Bean & Corn, Medium Garlic Cilantro, Mild)

Nature's Promise - Organic (Chipotle, Medium, Mild)

Newman's Own - Black Bean & Corn, Hot, Medium, Mild, Organic (Cilantro, Medium), Peach, Pineapple

Old Dutch - Restaurante Salsa (Medium, Mild)

Old El Paso - Salsa Thick N' Chunky (Hot, Medium, Mild)

Organicville - Medium, Mild, Pineapple

Ortega -
Garden Medium
Original (Medium, Mild)
Roasted Garlic
Salsa Verde
Thick & Chunky (Medium, Mild)

Pace -
Chunky Salsa (Medium, Mild)
Pico De Gallo

Publix -
All Natural (Hot, Medium, Mild)
Thick & Chunky (Hot, Medium, Mild)

Publix GreenWise Market - Organic (Medium, Mild)

Safeway Select - 3 Bean Medium, Garlic Lovers, Peach Pineapple Medium, Roasted Tomato Medium, Southwest (Hot, Medium, Mild), Verde Medium

Salpica -
Cilantro Green Olive
Fall Harvest
Garlic Chipotle
Habanero Lime
Mango Peach

Roasted Corn & Bean
Rustic Tomato
Spring Break
Summer Of Love
Tomato Jalapeno

Taco Bell - Thick 'N Chunky (Medium, Mild)

Tostitos -
All Natural
Hot Chunky
Medium Chunky
Mild Chunky

UTZ - Mt. Misery Mike's Salsa Dip, Sweet Salsa Dip

Wegmans Brand - Hot, Medium, Mild, Organic (Hot, Mango, Medium, Mild), Roasted (Chipotle, Salsa Verde, Sweet Pepper, Tomato), Santa Fe Style

Winn Dixie -
Black Bean & Corn (Medium)
Chunky (Medium, Mild)
Fire Roasted Pepper (Medium)
Roasted Chipotle
Roasted Green
Roasted Sweet Pepper
Roasted Tomato

Salt

Albertsons - Iodized, Regular

Great Value Brand (Wal-Mart) - Iodized, Plain

Hannaford Brand - Iodized, Regular

Kroger Brand

Manischewitz

Meijer Brand - Iodized, Plain

S   **Morton** - Coarse Kosher Salt, Iodized Table Salt, Lite Salt Mixture, Plain Table Salt, Salt Substitute, Sea Salt (Coarse, Fine)

Nu Salt - Salt Substitute

Publix

Safeway Brand - Iodized, Plain

Spartan Brand - Garlic, Iodized, Plain

Stop & Shop Brand - Iodized, Plain

Wegmans Brand - Iodized, Plain

Winn Dixie - Iodized, Plain

Sandwich Meat... see Deli Meat

Sardines... *All Fresh Fish Is Gluten/Casein/Soy Free (Non-Marinated, Unseasoned)*

Bumble Bee - Canned In Water

Chicken Of The Sea - In Mustard Sauce, In Water, Regular

Crown Prince -

Crosspacked Brisling In Olive Oil

One Layer Brisling In Mustard

Two Layer Brisling In Olive Oil

Crown Prince Natural - Skinless & Boneless In (Pure Olive Oil, Water)

Ocean Prince - In (Spring Water, Tomato Sauce)

Sauces... (includes Marinara, Pasta, Tomato, etc.)

A Taste Of Thai - Curry Paste (Green, Red, Yellow), Fish Sauce, Garlic Chili Pepper Sauce, Pad Thai, Peanut Satay Sauce, Sweet Red Chili Sauce

Amy's - Family Marinara, Low Sodium Marinara, Roasted Garlic, Tomato Basil (Low Sodium, Regular)

Bertolli -

Marinara w/Burgundy Wine

Tomato & Basil

Vidalia Onion w/Roasted Garlic

Bove's Of Vermont - All Natural (Marinara, Mushroom & Wine, Roasted Garlic)

S

Classico - Bruschetta Sauce (Basil & Tomato, Extra Garlic), Red Sauce (Tomato & Basil, Traditional Sweet Basil)

Colameco's - Pomodoro Sauce

Contadina -
Tomato Paste (Regular)
Tomato Sauce (Extra Thick & Zesty, Garlic & Onion Tomato, Regular, w/Italian Herbs)

Daddy Sam's - Bar B Que Sawce (Medium Ginger Jalapeno, Original), Salmon Glaze

Dave's Gourmet - Organic Red Heirloom, Spicy Heirloom Marinara

Del Monte - No Salt Added Tomato, Regular Tomato

Di Lusso - Sweet Onion Sauce

Eden Organic -
Apple Cherry Sauce
Spaghetti Sauce (No Salt Added, Regular)

Emeril's -
Pasta Sauce
Kicked Up Tomato
Sicilian Gravy

Fischer & Wieser -
Charred Pineapple Bourbon
Chipotle Sauce (Original Roasted Raspberry, Plum Chipotle BBQ, Pomegranate & Mango, Roasted Blackberry, Roasted Blueberry)
Mango Ginger Habanero
Papaya Lime Serrano
Steak & Grilling
Sweet & Savory Onion Glaze
Texas 1015 Onion Glaze
Traditional Steak & Grilling

Frank's RedHot - Chile 'N Lime, Original, Xtra Hot

S **Frontera** -
  Cocktail & Ceviche Sauce (Cilantro Lime, Tomato Chipotle)
  Cooking Sauce (Roasted Garlic & Chipotle, Roasted Tomato & Cilantro)
  Enchilada Sauce Chipotle Garlic
  Grilling Sauce (Chipotle Honey Mustard, Red Pepper Sesame)
  Hot Sauce (Chipotle, Habanero, Jalapeno, Red Pepper)
  Taco Sauce (Chipotle Garlic, Roasted Tomato)
Hannaford Brand - Tomato
Health Market - Mushroom Onion, Organic Tomato Basil
House Of Blues - Bayou Heat Hot Sauce
Hunt's -
  Organic Pasta Sauce (Regular, w/Roasted Garlic)
  Tomato Sauce (Basil Garlic & Oregano, Regular, Roasted Garlic)
Las Palmas - Red Chile, Red Enchilada
Lee Kum Kee - Panda Brand Green Label Oyster Flavored
Meijer Brand -
  Extra Chunky Spaghetti Sauce (Garden Combo, Mushroom & Green Pepper)
  Pasta Sauce Select (Marinara, Mushroom & Olive, Onion & Garlic, Original)
  Tomato Sauce (Regular, Organic)
Midwest Country Fare - Tomato Sauce
Moore's Marinade - Honey BBQ Wing, Original, Teriyaki
Mr. Spice Organic - Sauce & Marinade (Ginger Stir Fry, Honey BBQ, Indian Curry, Sweet & Sour, Thai Peanut)
Muir Glen - Organic (Beef Bolognese, Cabernet Marinara, Chunky Tomato & Herb, Fire Roasted Tomato, Garden Vegetable, Garlic Roasted Garlic, Italian Herb, Italian Sausage w/Peppers, Portabello Mushroom), Tomato Sauce (Chunky, No Salt Added, Regular)
Nature's Promise - Organic Pasta Sauce (Plain)
Newman's Own - Fra Diavolo

Patsy's Pasta Sauce - Marinara, Tomato Basil

Prego - Fresh Mushroom, Traditional

Publix - Tomato Sauce

Ragu - Light Tomato & Basil

Rao's - Homemade (Arrabbiata, Cuore Di Pomodoro, Marinara, Puttanesca, Roasted Eggplant, Southern Italian Pepper & Mushroom, Vodka)

Safeway Brand - Sloppy Joe

Safeway Select -

    Chili Sauce

    Gourmet Dipping Sauces (Honey Mustard, Sweet & Sour)

    Pasta Sauce

        Arrabiatta

        Chunky Vegetable

        Mushroom/Onion

        Roasted Garlic

        Spicy Red Bell Pepper

    Taco Sauce Mild

Sauces 'N Love - Arrabbiata, Barely Bolognese, Fresh Marinara & Pizza Sauces, Mint Pesto, Parsley Chimichurri, Pesto, Pink Pesto, Pomodoro & Basilico, Puttanesca, Sugo Rosa, Tuscan Vodka

Scarpetta -

    Arrabbiata

    Barely Bolognese

    Bruschetta Toppings (Tomato & Artichoke, Tomato & Capers)

    Fresh Marinara & Pizza Sauces

    Puttanesca

    Spreads (Artichoke & Olive, Asparagus, Olive & Almond, Red Pepper & Eggplant, Spicy Red Pepper)

    Tomato & Arugula

    Tuscan Vodka

S Seeds Of Change -
  Indian Simmer Sauce (Jalfrezi, Madras)
  Pasta Sauce
    Arrabiatta Di Roma
    Marinara Di Venezia
    Tomato Basil Genovese
    Tuscan Tomato & Garlic
Sharwood's -
  Kaffir Lime & Coriander
  Plum Sauce
  Sweet Chilli & Lemongrass
Simply Boulder - Culinary Sauce (Honey Dijon●, Pineapple Ginger●)
Spartan Brand - Chili, Sloppy Joe, Tomato Sauce
Stonewall Kitchen Sauce -
  Roasted Garlic Basil
  Traditional Marinara
Texas Pete -
  Garlic Hot Sauce
  Hotter Hot Sauce
  Original Hot Sauce
  Pepper
  Seafood
Thai Kitchen -
  Fish Sauce
  Simmer Sauce (Green Curry, Panang Curry, Red Curry)
  Spicy Thai Chili
  Sweet Red Chili
Walden Farms - Scampi
Wegmans Brand -
  Bruschetta Topping (Traditional Tomato)
  Italian Classics (Seasoned Tomato)

Lemon & Caper Sauce
Prepared Horseradish
Tomato Sauce

Wild Thymes -
Dipping Sauce
Indian Vindaloo
Moroccan Spicy Pepper
Thai Chili Roasted Garlic
Tropical Mango Lime Marinade

Winn Dixie -
Classic Fra Diavolo
Classic Style (Double Garlic, Fat Free)

Woodstock Farms - Tomato Sauce (Chunky, No Salt, Original)

Sauerkraut
B&G
Boar's Head
Cortland Valley Organic
Eden Organic - Organic
Flanagan
Great Value Brand (Wal-Mart) - Canned
Hannaford Brand
Hy-Vee - Shredded Kraut
Krrrrisp Kraut
Meijer Brand
Safeway Brand
Silver Floss
Spartan Brand
Wegmans Brand
Willie's
Winn Dixie

S Sausage

Abraham - Diced Prosciutto

Aidells -

Artichoke & Garlic

Cajun Style Andouille

Chicken & Apple Breakfast Links

Habanero & Green Chile

Mango

Smoked Chorizo

Applegate Farms -

Genoa Salami (Hot, Natural, Organic)

Joy Stick

Natural Uncured Hot Dogs (Beef, Big Apple, Chicken, Turkey)

Organic (Andouille, Chicken & Apple, Fire Roasted Red Pepper, Smoked Pork Andouille, Smoked Pork Bratwurst, Smoked Pork Kielbasa, Sweet Italian)

Organic Uncured Hot Dogs (Beef, Chicken, Stadium Style, Organic, Turkey)

Pancetta

Pepperoni

Sopressata (Hot, Regular)

The Greatest Little Organic Smokey Pork Cocktail Franksi

Turkey Salami

Butterball - Turkey Sausage (Fresh Bratwurst, Fresh Breakfast, Fresh Hot Italian, Fresh Sweet Italian, Polska Kielbasa Dinner, Smoked Dinner, Smoked, Smoked Hot)

Canino's -

Bratwurst●

Breakfast Sausage●

German Brand Sausage●

Hot Chorizo●

Hot Italian Sausage●

Mild Italian Sausage●

Polish Sausage●

Spicy Cajun Style Sausage●

Sweet Italian Sausage●

Dietz & Watson -

Beef Franks (New York Deli) *(Except Fat Free & Gourmet Lite)*

Black Forest Knockwurst

Bratwurst

Honey Roll

Lunch Roll

Pepper & Onion Sausage

Wieners

Eckrich - Franks (Beef, Original)

Empire Kosher - Deli Slices (Turkey Bologna, Turkey Salami), Turkey Franks

Farmer John -

Breakfast Sausage Links & Patties (Firehouse Hot Roll, Firehouse Hot Skinless Links, Old Fashioned Maple Skinless, Original Roll, Original Skinless, Premium Original Chorizo, Premium PC Links Lower Fat, Premium Sausage Patties Lower Fat, Premium SC Links, Premium Spicy Hot Chorizo, Premium Traditional Chorizo, Quick Serve Fully Cooked)

California Natural Chicken Sausage (Apple Chicken Smoked, Cajun Style Smoked, Chicken Brat Smoked, Lemon Cracked Pepper Chicken Smoked, Mango & Habanero Smoked)

Cotto Salami

Dinner Sausage (Hot Louisiana Smoked, Jalapeno Pepper Premium Rope, Jalapeno Pepper Premium Smoked, Premium Beef Rope, Premium Polish, Premium Pork Rope, Red Hots Extra Hot Premium Smoked)

Franks & Wieners (Dodger Dogs, Premium Beef Franks, Premium Jumbo Beef Franks, Premium Jumbo Meat Wieners, Premium Meat Wieners, Premium Quarter Pounder Beef Franks)

S   **Garrett County Farms -**
Andouille Sausage
Chorizo Sausage
Franks (4XL Big Beef, Chicken, Old Fashioned Beef, Original Deli, Premium Beef, Turkey)
Kielbasa (Polska, Turkey)
Sliced Beef (Bologna, Salami)
Sliced Uncured Pepperoni

Hertel's - All Original Fresh Sausages *(Except British Bangers)*

Hillshire Farms -
Lit'l Beef Franks
Lit'l Polskas
Lit'l Smokies Beef
Lit'l Wieners
Turkey Smoked Sausage

Homeland - Hard Salami

Honeysuckle White -
Hardwood Smoked Turkey Franks
Hickory Smoked Cooked Turkey Salami
Turkey Sausage (Bratwurst, Breakfast Sausage (Links, Patties), Italian Sausage (Hot, Sweet), Poblano Pepper Links)
Turkey Sausage Rolls (Breakfast, Mild Italian)

Hormel -
Deli Sliced Cooked Pastrami
Little Sizzlers (Links, Patties)
Natural Choice (Hard Salami, Pepperoni)
Smokies
Pepperoni (Pillow Pack, Sliced)

Hy-Vee - Beef, Cooked Salami, Little Smokies (Beef, Regular), Polish (Link, Rope), Smoked Bratwurst

Ian's - Wheat Free Gluten Free Recipe Popcorn Turkey Corn Dogs

sausage

S

Jennie-O Turkey Store -

Fresh

> Breakfast Sausage (Mild Links, Mild Patties)

> Dinner Sausage (Hot Italian, Lean Turkey Bratwurst, Sweet Italian)

Frozen Italian Style Meatballs

Turkey Franks

Jimmy Dean -

All Natural Pork Roll Sausage (Hot, Regular)

Fully Cooked Links (Original, Turkey)

Fully Cooked Patties (Hot, Original, Sandwich Size, Turkey)

Original (Links, Patties)

Premium Pork Roll Sausage (Bold Country, Extra Mild Country, Hot, Italian, Light, Maple, Mild Country, Regular, Sage)

Johnsonville -

Bratwurst (Butcher Shop Style Cooked, Hot 'N Spicy, Original, Smoked, Stadium Style)

Butcher Shop Style Wieners

Chorizo

Hearty Beef Bologna

Irish O'Garlic

Italian (Hot, Mild, Sweet)

Italian Ground Sausage (Hot, Mild, Sweet)

New Orleans Brand Smoked

Original (Breakfast (Links, Patties), Ring Bologna)

Polish

Vermont Maple Syrup (Links, Patties)

Jones Dairy Farm -

All Natural

> Hearty Pork Sausage Links●

> Light Pork Sausage and Rice Links●

S

> Little Link Pork Sausage●
>
> Maple Sausage Patties●
>
> Original Pork Roll Sausage●
>
> Pork Sausage Patties●
>
> All Natural Golden Brown Cooked & Browned Sausage Patties (Maple Fully●, Mild Fully●)
>
> All Natural Golden Brown Fully Cooked & Browned Turkey●
>
> All Natural Golden Brown Light Fully Cooked & Browned Sausage & Rice Links●
>
> All Natural Golden Fully Cooked & Browned Sausage Links (Made From Beef●, Maple●, Mild●, Spicy●)

Lou's Famous - Chicken Sausage (Apple, Peppers & Onion, Roasted Red Pepper & Garlic, Spicy Italian, Sundried Tomato)

Maluma - All Bison Sausage

Midwest Country Fare - Hot Dogs, Sliced Cooked Salami

Nature's Promise -

> Mild Italian Chicken
>
> Spiced Apple Chicken
>
> Sun Dried Tomato & Basil Chicken

Organic Prairie - Frozen Organic (Bratwurst 12 oz., Breakfast Sausage 12 oz., Brown N Serve Breakfast Links 8 oz., Italian Sausage 12 oz.)

Oscar Mayer -

> Beef Franks (Bun Length, Jumbo, Light, Regular)
>
> Little Wieners
>
> Mini Beef Hot Dogs
>
> Salami (Cotto, Deli Thin Beef, Hard)
>
> Summer Sausage (Beef, Regular)
>
> Turkey Franks (Bun Length, Regular)
>
> Wieners (98 % Fat Free, Bun Length, Jumbo, Light, Regular, Turkey Franks)
>
> XXL Hot Dogs (Deli Style Beef, Hot & Spicy, Premium Beef)

S

Primo Naturale -
Chorizo (Sliced Dried, Stick Dried)
Chub Salami (Genoa, Original, w/Black Pepper, w/Herbs)
Pepperoni (Pillow Pack, Sliced Dried, Stick, Whole Large Diameter)
Sliced Salami (Hard, Original, Premium Genoa, w/Black Pepper, w/Herbs)
Sopressata (Regular, Sliced)
Whole Chorizo
Whole Salami (Black Pepper, Genoa, Hard, Herb & Wine, Original)

Primo Taglio - Salami (Peppered Coated w/Gelatin & Black Pepper)

Publix -
Bratwurst
Chorizo
Franks (Beef, Meat)
Fresh Turkey Italian (Hot, Mild)
Hot Dogs (Beef, Meat)
Italian (Hot, Mild)

Publix GreenWise Market - Pork Sage Sausage

Safeway Select -
Beef Franks
Bratwurst
Italian (Hot, Mild, Pork)
Polish
Regular Hot Dogs

Shelton's -
Bologna Uncured Turkey
Franks (Smoked Chicken, Smoked Turkey, Uncured Chicken, Uncured Turkey)
Turkey Sausage (Breakfast, Italian, Patties)
Turkey Sticks (Pepperoni, Regular)

S **SPAM -** Classic, Less Sodium, Lite, Oven Roasted Turkey, Smoke Flavored

Spartan Brand - Breakfast (Maple, Original), Hot, Mild

Thrifty Maid - Vienna Sausage (Chicken, Original)

Wegmans Brand -

Beef Hot Dogs (Skinless)

Red Hot Dogs Skinless (Lite)

Uncured Beef Hot Dogs (Skinless)

Wellshire Farms -

Beef Franks Hot Dogs (4XL Big, The Old Fashioned, The Premium)

Cocktail Franks

Frozen

Chicken Apple Sausage (Links, Patties)

Country Sage Sausage (Links, Patties)

Original Breakfast Sausage (Links, Patties)

Sunrise Maple Sausage (Links, Patties)

Turkey (Burgers, Maple Sausage (Links, Patties))

Morning Maple Turkey Breakfast Link Sausage

Original Matt's Select Pepperoni Steaks

Polska Kielbasa

Pork Andouille Sausage

Pork Sausage (Chorizo, Linguica)

Sliced (Beef Pepperoni, Beef Salami)

Smoked Bratwurst

The Original Deli Franks

Turkey

Andouille Sausage

Dinner Link Sausage Mild Italian Style

Franks

Kielbasa

Tom Toms (Hot & Spicy, Original)

seasonings

S

Wellshire Organic - Organic (Andouille Sausage (Pork, Turkey), Franks (Beef, Chicken, Turkey), Kielbasa (Polska, Turkey))

Scallops... *All Fresh Seafood Is Gluten/Casein/Soy Free (Non-Marinated, Unseasoned)*

Hy-Vee - Frozen

Publix - Sea Scallops

Whole Catch - Sea Scallops

Seafood Sauce

Frontera - Cocktail & Ceviche Sauce (Cilantro Lime, Tomato Chipotle)

Hannaford Brand - Cocktail Sauce

Lou's Famous - Cocktail Sauce

McCormick - Extra Hot, Gold Dipt (Regular), Original, Seafood Sauce (Cajun Style, Mediterranean, Santa Fe Style)

Texas Pete - Seafood Cocktail

Walden Farms

Seasoning Packets... see Seasonings

Seasonings

Accent - Flavor Enhancer (All Varieties)

Albertsons - Bay Leaves, Black Pepper, Cinnamon, Garlic Powder, Garlic Salt, Ginger, Nutmeg, Onion, Onion Powder, Paprika, Parsley Flakes

Arora Creations -

Organic Seasoning Packets (Bhindi Masala, Gobi, Punjabi Chhole, Rajmah, Tandoori Chicken)

Regular Seasoning Packets (Bhindi Masala, Chicken Tikka Masala, Goan Shrimp Curry, Gobi, Punjabi Chhole, Rajmah, Tandoori Chicken, Tikka Masala)

Bone Suckin' - Seasoning & Rub

Bragg - Sea Kelp Delight, Sprinkle Seasoning

Cali Fine Foods▲ - Gourmet Seasoning Packets (Dill Delight●, Garlic Gusto●, Herb Medley●, Spicy Fiesta●, Sweet & Spicy BBQ●)

S   **Chi-Chi's** - Fiesta Restaurante Seasoning Mix

Durkee - All Food Coloring, All Liquid Extracts, All Liquid Flavorings, Allspice, Alum, Anise Seed, Arrowroot, Basil, Bay Leaves, Caraway Seed, Cardamom, Cayenne Pepper, Celery Salt, Celery Seed, Chicken Seasoning, Chili Powder, Chives, Cilantro, Cinnamon, Cloves, Coriander, Cream Of Tartar, Crushed Red Pepper, Cumin, Curry Powder, Dill Seed/Weed, Fennel, Garlic Minced, Garlic Pepper, Garlic Powder, Garlic Salt, Ginger, Italian Seasoning, Jamaican Jerk Seasoning, Lemon Pepper, Lime Pepper, Mace, Marjoram, Meat Tenderizer, Mint Leaves, MSG, Mustard, Nutmeg, Onion Minced, Onion Powder, Onion Salt, Oregano, Paprika, Parsley, Pepper Black/White (All), Pickling Spice, Poppy Seed, Rosemary, Sage, Salt Free Garden Seasoning, Salt Free Garlic & Herb, Salt Free Lemon Pepper, Salt Free Original All Purpose Seasoning, Salt Free Vegetable Seasoning, Sesame Seed, Six Pepper Blend, Steak Seasoning, Tarragon, Thyme, Turmeric

Emeril's -

Essence (Bayou Blast, Italian, Original, Southwest)

Rubs (Chicken, Fish, Rib, Steak, Turkey)

Food Club Brand - Black Pepper, Cinnamon, Iodized Salt, Pure Vanilla Extract, Salt

Gayelord Hauser - Spike Magic (5 Herb, Garlic)

Hannaford Brand -

Basil Leaves, Bay Leaves, Celery Salt, Chili Powder, Crushed Red Pepper, Garlic Powder, Garlic Salt, Ground Black Pepper, Ground Cinnamon, Ground Ginger, Ground Mustard, Ground Nutmeg, Minced Onion, Oregano Leaves, Paprika

Rubs (Bayou Cajun, Cabo Chipotle, Chicago Steakhouse, Fisherman's Wharf, Monterey Citrus Pepper, Mushroom Truffle, Northwoods Garlic Pepper, Sweet Southern BBQ)

Hy-Vee - Basil Leaf, Bay Leaves, Black Pepper, Chicken Grill Seasoning, Chili Powder, Chopped Onion, Dill Weed, Garlic Powder, Garlic Salt, Grinders (Black Peppercorn, Peppercorn Melange, Sea Salt), Ground Cinnamon, Ground Cloves, Ground Mustard, Iodized Salt, Italian Seasoning, Lemon Pepper, Meat Tenderizer, Oregano Leaf, Paprika, Parsley Flakes, Plain Salt, Red

S

Crushed Pepper, Rosemary, Salt & Pepper Shaker, Seasoned Salt, Steak Grilling Seasoning, Thyme

Konriko - Chipotle All Purpose Seasoning, Creole Seasoning

Laura Lynn - Black Pepper

Lawry's -

Black Peppered Seasoned Salt, Seasoned Pepper, The Original Seasoned Salt *(No Soy Lecithin)*

Seasoning Mixes (Guacamole, Tenderizing Beef Marinade Mix)

Litehouse - Freeze Dried (Basil, Chives, Cilantro, Dill, Garlic, Parsley)

Lowes Foods Brand - Black Pepper, Cinnamon Ground, Paprika, Salt & Pepper Shaker Set

Mayacamas - Chicken BBQ, Curry Blend, Herb Mix, Savory Salt

McCormick -

Grill Mates Dry Rub (Chicken, Pork, Steak, Sweet Smoky)

Grill Mates Grinders (Montreal Chicken Seasoning, Montreal Steak Seasoning)

Grill Mates Seasoning Blends (25% Less Sodium Montreal Chicken, 25 % Less Sodium Montreal Steak, Barbecue, Mesquite)

Roasting Rub (Cracked Peppercorn Herb, French Herb, Savory Herb)

Seasoning Packets (Fajitas, Salsa, Tex Mex Chili)

Spices (Alum, Anise Seed, Apple Pie Spice, Basil Leaves, Bay Leaves, Caraway Seed, Celery Flakes, Celery Seed, Chili Powder, Chives, Cilantro Leaves, Cinnamon Sticks, Cinnamon Sugar, Cream Of Tartar, Cumin Seed, Curry Powder, Dill Seed, Dill Weed, Fennel Seed, Ground Allspice, Ground Cinnamon, Ground Cloves, Ground Cumin, Ground Ginger, Ground Mace, Ground Marjoram, Ground Mustard, Ground Nutmeg, Ground Oregano, Ground Sage, Ground Thyme, Ground Turmeric, Hot Mexican Style, Italian Seasoning, Marjoram Leaves, Mixed Pickling Spice, Mustard Seed, Oregano, Oregano Leaves, Paprika, Parsley Flakes, Poppy Seed, Poultry Seasoning, Pumpkin Pie Spice, Rosemary Leaves, Rubbed Sage, Sage Leaves, Sesame Seed, Tarragon Leaves, Whole Allspice, Whole Cloves, Whole Mexican)

S

Meijer Brand - Black Pepper, Chili Powder, Cinnamon, Garlic Powder, Garlic Salt, Onion, Onion Salt, Oregano Leaves, Paprika, Parsley Flakes, Seasoned Salt

Midwest Country Fare - Chili Powder, Chopped Onion, Cinnamon, Garlic Powder, Garlic Salt, Ground Black Pepper, Onion Powder, Parsley Flakes, Pure Ground Black Pepper, Season Salt

Morton -

Canning & Pickling Salt

Hot Salt

Lite Salt Mixture

Nature's Seasons Seasoning Blend

Popcorn Salt

Salt & Pepper Shakers

Sausage & Meat Loaf Seasoning

Seasoned Salt

Smoke Flavored Sugar Cure

Sugar Cure

Tender Quick

Mrs. Dash - Caribbean Citrus, Extra Spicy, Fiesta Lime, Garlic & Herb, Grilling Blends, Lemon Pepper, Onion & Herb, Original Blend, Southwest Chipotle, Table Blend, Tomato Basil Garlic

Nantucket Off Shore - Rub (Bayou, Dragon, Garden, Holiday Turkey, Mt. Olympus, Nantucket, Prairie, Pueblo, Raj, Rasta, Renaissance, St. Remy), Shellfish Boil

Nielsen-Massey - Madagascar Bourbon Pure Vanilla Powder●

O Organics - Basil Leaves, Bay Leaves, Cayenne Peppers, Ground Cinnamon, Ground Cloves, Ground Cumin, Ground Nutmeg, Paprika

Old Bay - 30% Less Sodium, Blackened Seasoning, Garlic & Herb, Lemon & Herb, Original, Rub, Seafood Steamer

Ortega - Chipotle Mix, Taco Seasoning Mix

Publix - Adobo Seasoning w/Pepper, Adobo Seasoning w/o Pepper, Ajoen Polvo Garlic Powder, Basil, Bay Leaves, Black Pepper, Chili Powder, Cinnamon, Comino Molido Ground

Cumin, Condimento Completo Seasoning, Garlic Powder, Garlic **S**
Powder w/Parsley, Garlic Salt, Ground Cumin, Ground Ginger,
Ground Mustard, Ground Nutmeg, Ground Red Pepper, Italian
Seasonings, Minced Onion, Onion Powder, Oregano, Paprika,
Parsley Flakes, Salt, Seasoned Salt, Whole Black Pepper

Safeway Brand - Fajita Seasoning Mix

Sharwood's - Curry Powder (Hot, Medium, Mild)

Spartan Brand - Black Pepper, Chili Powder, Cinnamon, Garlic
Powder, Garlic Salt, Ground Nutmeg, Imitation Vanilla, Iodized
Salt, Iodized Salt Crystals, Minced Onion, Oregano Leaves,
Paprika, Parsley Flakes, Salt, Vanilla Extract

Spice Islands - All Food Coloring, All Liquid Extracts, All Liquid
Flavorings, Allspice, Alum, Anise Seed, Arrowroot, Basil, Bay
Leaves, Caraway Seed, Cardamom, Cayenne Pepper, Celery Salt,
Celery Seed, Chicken Seasoning, Chili Powder, Chives, Cilantro,
Cinnamon, Cloves, Coriander, Cream Of Tartar, Crushed Red
Pepper, Cumin, Curry Powder, Dill Seed/Weed, Fennel, Garlic
Minced, Garlic Pepper, Garlic Powder, Garlic Salt, Ginger, Italian
Seasoning, Jamaican Jerk Seasoning, Lemon Pepper, Lime Pepper,
Mace, Marjoram, Meat Tenderizer, Mint Leaves, MSG, Mustard,
Nutmeg, Onion Minced, Onion Powder, Onion Salt, Oregano,
Paprika, Parsley, Pepper Black/White (All), Pickling Spice, Poppy
Seed, Rosemary, Sage, Salt Free Garden Seasoning, Salt Free
Garlic & Herb, Salt Free Lemon Pepper, Salt Free Original All
Purpose Seasoning, Salt Free Vegetable Seasoning, Sesame Seed, Six
Pepper Blend, Steak Seasoning, Tarragon, Thyme, Turmeric

Spice Islands Specialty - Beau Monde, Chili Powder, Crystallized Ginger,
Fine Herbs, Italian Herb Seasoning, Old Hickory Smoked Salt

Tones - All Food Coloring, All Liquid Extracts, All Liquid Flavorings,
Allspice, Alum, Anise Seed, Arrowroot, Basil, Bay Leaves, Caraway
Seed, Cardamom, Cayenne Pepper, Celery Salt, Celery Seed,
Chicken Seasoning, Chili Powder, Chives, Cilantro, Cinnamon,
Cloves, Coriander, Cream Of Tartar, Crushed Red Pepper, Cumin,
Curry Powder, Dill Seed/Weed, Fennel, Garlic Minced, Garlic
Pepper, Garlic Powder, Garlic Salt, Ginger, Italian Seasoning,
Jamaican Jerk Seasoning, Lemon Pepper, Lime Pepper, Mace,

S Marjoram, Meat Tenderizer, Mint Leaves, MSG, Mustard, Nutmeg, Onion Minced, Onion Powder, Onion Salt, Oregano, Paprika, Parsley, Pepper Black/White (All), Pickling Spice, Poppy Seed, Rosemary, Sage, Salt Free Garden Seasoning, Salt Free Garlic & Herb, Salt Free Lemon Pepper, Salt Free Original All Purpose Seasoning, Salt Free Vegetable Seasoning, Sesame Seed, Six Pepper Blend, Steak Seasoning, Tarragon, Thyme, Turmeric

Tropical Sun Spices - Caribbean Garlic Lemon Herb, Caribbean Guava Delite, Caribbean Seasoning Salt, Caribbean Tangerine Pepper, Citrus Delite Spice, Creole Spice, Cuban Rum Spice, Fisherman's Seasoning, Jamaican Black Pepper, Key Lime Jerk Seasoning, Mesquite Grilling Spice, Pizza Pasta Spice, Salsa Seasoning Spice, Sexy Spice, Spanish Sazon Completa, Southwest Santa Fe Spice, Strawberry Spice Rub, Sweet Orange Habanero Spice

Watkins - Organic Beef Seasoning

Weber Grill Creations -

Club Pack Seasoning (Smokey Mesquite)

Grinders (Chicago Steak, N'Orleans Cajun, Smokey Mesquite, Veggie Grill)

Seasoning (Chicago Steak, Mango Lime, N'Orleans Cajun, Roasted Garlic & Herb, Seasoning Salt, Smokey Mesquite, Veggie Grill)

Wegmans Brand - Bay Leaves, Black Pepper, Cinnamon, Cloves, Cracked Pepper Blend, Fleur De Sel (Sea Salt), Minced Onions, Nutmeg, Oregano, Paprika, Parsley Flakes, Sage (Ground & Rubbed)

Seaweed -

Eden Organic - Agar Agar Bars, Agar Agar Flakes

Nagai's - Sushi Nori Roasted Seaweed

Yaki - Sushi Nori Roasted Seaweed

Yamamotoyama - Sushi Party Toasted Seaweed, Toasted Seaweed Nori

Seeds

Arrowhead Mills - Flax, Golden Flax, Mechanically Hulled Sesame, Sunflower, Unhulled Sesame

Durkee - Anise, Caraway, Celery, Dill, Poppy, Sesame

Eden Organic - Pumpkin (Dry Roasted & Salted)

Frito Lay - Flamin' Hot Flavored Sunflower Seeds, Sunflower Seed Kernels, Sunflower Seeds

Goraw - Seeds (Sprouted Pumpkin●, Sprouted Sunflower●), Seed Mix (Simple●, Spicy●)

Meijer Brand - Sunflower (Plain, Salted In Shell)

Publix - Sunflower Seeds

Shiloh Farms - Black Sesame Seeds

Spice Island - Anise, Caraway, Celery, Dill, Poppy, Sesame

Tones - Anise, Caraway, Celery, Dill, Poppy, Sesame

Woodstock Farms -

Non Organic Seeds (Pumpkin (Regular, Roasted Salted)), Sunflower Hulled (Regular, Roasted No Salt, Roasted Salted)

Organic Seeds (Flax, Pumpkin, Sesame, Sunflower (Hulled, Hulled Roasted No Salt, Roasted & Salted), White Quinoa)

Sesame Oil... see Oil

Sesame Seeds... see Seeds

Shakes... see also Smoothies

Amazake -

Almond

Amazing Mango

Banana Appeal

Chocolate Almond

Cool Coconut

Go (Go Green, Hazelnuts)

Oh So Original

Rice Nog

Tiger Chai

Vanilla Pecan Pie

S Shortening

    Spectrum - Organic Palm Oil Shortening

    Shrimp... **All **Fresh** Seafood Is **Gluten/Casein/Soy Free (Non-Marinated, Unseasoned)***

    Captain's Choice - Cooked Tail On Shrimp

    Chicken Of The Sea - All Shrimp Products

    Crown Prince - Shrimp (Broken, Tiny)

    Great Value Brand (Wal-Mart) - Canned Tiny Shrimp

    Hy-Vee - Frozen Cooked, Platter

    Publix - Cooked (All Sizes), Fresh (All Sizes)

    Publix GreenWise Market - All Sizes (Cooked, Fresh)

    Starfish - Just Grilled Shrimp●

    Wegmans - Shrimp From Belize Uncooked

    Shrimp Sauce... see Cocktail Sauce

    Sloppy Joe/Sloppy Joe Sauce

    Hannaford Brand

    Heinz

    Hormel - Not So Sloppy Joe

    Hy-Vee

    Meijer Brand - Sloppy Joe Sauce

    Safeway

    Spartan Brand

    Winn Dixie - Sloppy Joe Sauce

    Smoke

    Colgin - Natural Liquid Smoke (Apple, Hickory, Mesquite, Pepper)

    Wright's - Liquid Smoke (Hickory, Mesquite)

    Smoked Sausage... see Sausage

    Smoked Turkey... see Turkey

    Smoothies... see also Shakes

    Ella's Kitchen - Smoothie Fruits (The Green One, The Purple One, The Red One, The Yellow One)

Hansen's Smoothie Nectar - Energy Island Blast, Guava Strawberry, Mango Pineapple, Peach Berry, Pineapple Coconut, Strawberry Banana **S**

Snacks

Annie's▲ - Organic Bunny Fruit Snacks (Berry Patch, Tropical Treat)

Baken-Ets - Pork Skins (BBQ, Fried)

Betty Lou's - Krispy Bites, Nut Butter Balls Chocolate Walnut

Deep River Snacks - Mesquite BBQ, Original Salted, Reduced Fat Original Salted, Salt & Cracked Pepper, Sweet Maui Onion, Sweet Maui Onion Baked Fries

Eat Smart - Veggie Crisps Regular

Eden Organic - All Mixed Up (Regular), Wild Berry Mix

Glenny's - Brown Rice Marshmallow Treat (Chocolate●, Peanut Caramel●, Raspberry Jubilee●, Vanilla●)

Goraw -

Flax Snax (Pizza●, Simple●, Spicy●, Sunflower●)

Ginger Snaps●

Granola (Apple Cinnamon●, Live●, Live Chocolate●, Simple●), Seed Mix (Simple●, Spicy●)

Seeds (Sprouted Pumpkin●, Sprouted Sunflower●)

Super Chips (Pumpkin●, Spirulina●)

Herr's - Pork Rinds (BBQ Flavored, Original)

Hy-Vee -

Nut Trail Mix (Raisin)

Tropical Fruit Mix

Mareblu Naturals -

Crunch (Almond, Almond Coconut, Cashew, Cashew Coconut, CranMango Cashew, Pecan Cinnamon, Pistachio)

Trail Mix Crunch (Blueberry Pomegranate, Cranberry Pomegranate, Cranblueberry Trail, Cranstrawberry Trail, Pecan Trail, Pistachio Trail)

S **Meijer Brand** -
  Fruit Rolls
    Justice League Galactic Berry
    Rescue Heroes
    Strawberry (Garfield, Regular)
    Wildberry Rush
  Fruit Snacks
    African Safari
    Curious George
    Jungle Adventure
    Justice League (Big Box, Regular)
    Mixed Fruit
    Peanuts
    Rescue Heroes Big Box
    Underwater World
    Variety Pack (Big Boy, Regular)
Mrs. May's Naturals - Crunch (Almond●, Black Sesame●, Cashew●, Coconut Almond●, Cran Blueberry●, Cran Tropical●, Pom Raspberry●, Pumpkin●, Strawberry Pineapple●, Sunflower●, Ultimate●, Walnut●, White Sesame●)
Nonuttin' Foods▲ - Fruit Snacks, Sulfite Free Dried Apples
Nu-World Foods - Mini Ridges (Rosemary Basil●, Sun Dried Tomato●)
Original Tings - Crunchy Corn Sticks
Oskri Organics - Almond Honey Crunch, Cashew Honey Crunch w/Cranberries, Pecan Honey Crunch w/Cinnamon
Pirate's Booty - Barbeque, Veggie
Spartan Brand - Fruit Snacks (Build A Bear, Curious George, Maya Miquel)
True North - Almond Clusters, Almonds Pistachios Walnut Pecans, Peanut Clusters (Pecan Almond, Regular)
Winn Dixie - Pork Rinds (BBQ, Hot, Regular)
Wise - Onion Flavored Rings

soda pop/carbonated beverages

S

Woodstock Farms - Organic Snack Mixes (California Supreme, Campfire, Cape Cod Cranberry, Cascade, Cranberry (Cove, Walnut Cashew), Goji Berry Power, Gourmet Trail, In The Raw, Organic, Tropical Delight, Tropical Fruit)

Snaps

Edward & Sons - Brown Rice Snaps (Onion Garlic, Plain (Unsalted), Salsa, Sesame (Unsalted), Toasted Onion, Vegetable)

Soda Pop/Carbonated Beverages

7up - All Varieties

A & W - Root Beer

Aquafina - FlavorSplash (Citrus Blend, Raspberry, Wild Berry)

Boylan's - Soda (Bottleworks, Seltzers)

Canada Dry -
Club Soda (All Varieties)
Ginger Ale (Diet, Regular)
Tonic Water (All Varieties)

Coca-Cola -
Cherry Coke (Diet, Regular, Zero)
Classic Coke (Caffeine Free, Regular, w/Lime, Zero)
Diet Coke (Caffeine Free, Plus, Regular, w/Lime, w/Splenda)
Vanilla Coke (Regular, Zero)

Crush - Grape, Pineapple, Strawberry

Dasani - Essence, Regular

Dr. Pepper -
Caffeine Free (Diet, Regular)
Cherry Vanilla (Diet, Regular)
Diet
Regular

Enviga - Sparkling Green Tea (Berry, Green)

Fanta - Grape

Full Throttle

S **Hannaford Brand** - Cola, Cream Soda, Ginger Ale, Grape, Lemon Lime, Orange, Orange Pineapple, Peach, Root Beer, Strawberry

Hansen's - All Sodas

Hires - Root Beer

Hy-Vee -

Black Cherry (Diet, Regular)

Cherry Cola

Club Soda

Cola (Diet, Regular)

Cream Soda

Diet Tonic

Dr. Hy Vee

Fruit Punch (Coolers, Regular)

Grape

Hee Haw (Diet, Regular)

Lemon Lime

Root Beer (Diet, Regular)

Strawberry

Tonic Water

Water Cooler (Black Cherry, Key Lime, Kiwi Strawberry, Mixed Berry, Peach, Peach Melba, Raspberry, Strawberry, White Grape)

I.B.C. - Root Beer

Orangina - Sparkling Citrus Beverage

Pepsi -

Caffeine Free (Diet, Regular)

Lime (Diet, Regular)

One

Pepsi (Diet, Regular)

Publix -

Black Cherry Soda

Cherry Cola

soda pop/carbonated beverages

Club Soda
Cola (Caffeine Free, Regular)
Cream Soda
Diet (Cola, Ginger Ale, Tonic Water)
Dr. Publix
Fruit Punch
Ginger Ale
Grape Soda
Lemon Lime Seltzer
Lemon Lime Soda (Diet, Regular)
Raspberry Seltzer
Root Beer (Diet, Regular)
Seltzer
Tonic Water

Safeway Select - Clear Sparkling Water (Cranberry Raspberry, Grapefruit Tangerine, Key Lime, Raspberry Black Cherry, Strawberry Kiwi, Strawberry Watermelon, Tangerine Lime, Wild Cherry)

Schweppes - All Varieties

Sierra Mist -

Cranberry Splash (Diet, Regular)
Free
Regular
Ruby
Splash (Diet, Regular)

Slice - Grape, Red

Sprite - Diet, Regular, Zero

Sunkist - Cherry Limeade, Grape, Strawberry

Tab - All Varieties

Tubz - Diet Root Beer

Vernors - Diet, Regular

Virgil's - Root Beer

S   Wegmans Brand -
Frizzante European Soda
Blood Orange
Blueberry Lemon
Sicilian Lemon
Sour Cherry Lemon
Soda
Black Cherry
Cherry (Regular, Wedge Diet)
Club Soda
Cola (Caffeine Free, Caffeine Free Diet, Diet, Lime, Regular)
Diet (Lime)
Dr. W (Diet, Regular)
Fountain Root Beer (Diet, Regular)
Ginger Ale (Diet, Regular)
Green Apple Sparkling Soda (Diet, Regular)
Mango
Tonic (Diet, Regular)
W UP (Diet, Regular)
Wedge Diet (Cherry Grapefruit)
Sparkling Beverage
Black Cherry
Cranberry Raspberry (Diet, Regular)
Key Lime (Diet, Regular)
Kiwi Strawberry (Diet, Regular)
Lemonade
Mixed Berry (Diet, Regular)
Peach (Diet, Diet Wedge, Grapefruit (Diet, Regular), Regular)
Sparkling Beverage w/Sweeteners (Black Cherry, Key Lime,
Tangerine Lime, White Grape)

soda pop/carbonated beverages

S

Welch's -
- Fruit Punch
- Grape
- Pineapple
- Strawberry

Winn Dixie -
- Black Cherry Soda
- Club Soda
- Cola (Caffeine Free, Cherry, Diet Vanilla, Regular, Vanilla)
- Cream Soda
- Diet (Chek, Kountry Mist Soda, Lemon Lime, Root Beer, Strawberry Soda, Vanilla Cola)
- Ginger Ale
- Grape Soda
- Green Apple Soda
- Kountry Mist Soda
- Lemonade
- Lemon Lime Soda
- Peach Soda
- Premium Draft Style Root Beer
- Punch
- Red Alerts Soda
- Red Cream Soda
- Root Beer
- Seltzer Water
- Sparkling Water (Country Strawberry, Green Apple, Key Lime, Mandarin Orange, Mellow Peach, White Grape, Wild Cherry, Zesty Raspberry)
- Strawberry Soda

S Sorghum
  Shiloh Farms - Sorghum Grain
Soup
  Amy's -
    Black Bean Vegetable
    Chunky Vegetable
    Fire Roasted Southwestern Vegetable
    Lentil (Curried, Light Sodium, Regular)
    Lentil Vegetable (Light Sodium, Regular)
    Split Pea (Light In Sodium, Regular)
    Tuscan Bean & Rice
  Baxters -
    Favorites
      Chicken Broth
      Cock A Leekie
      French Onion
      Lentil & Bacon
      Pea & Ham
      Scotch Vegetable
    Healthy Choice
      Chicken & Vegetable
      Chunky (Chicken & Vegetable Casserole, Country Vegetable)
      Tomato & Brown Lentil
    Luxury Consomme (Beef, Chicken)
    Soup Bowl (Smoked Bacon & Mixed Bean Soup)
  Dinty Moore - Beef Stew
  Dr. McDougall's - Black Bean, Black Bean & Lime, Chunky Tomato, Lentil, Roasted Red Pepper, Tamale w/Baked Chips, Tortilla w/Baked Chips, Vegetable
  Full Flavor Foods▲ - Soup Mix (Chicken●)
  Fungus Among Us - Organic Soup Mix (Moroccan Porcini & Green Lentil, Spicy Shiitake & Vegetable)

Health Valley -

Fat Free (5 Bean Vegetable, 14 Garden Vegetable, Black Bean & Vegetable, Corn & Vegetable, Lentil & Carrots, Split Pea & Carrots, Tomato Vegetable)

Organic (Lentil, Potato & Leek, Split Pea)

Organic No Salt Added (Black Bean, Lentil, Potato Leek, Split Pea, Tomato, Vegetable)

Imagine -

Organic Canned

Southwestern Tortilla

Organic Creamy

Acorn Squash & Mango

Butternut Squash

Corn & Lemongrass

Garden Broccoli

Garden Tomato Light In Sodium

Harvest Corn Light In Sodium

Potato Leek

Red Bliss Potato Light In Sodium

Sweet Potato (Light In Sodium, Regular)

Tomato

Kettle Cuisine - Angus Beef Steak Chili w/Beans●, Chicken Soup w/Rice Noodles●, Organic Carrot & Coriander Soup●, Roasted Vegetable Soup●, Three Bean Chili●, Tomato Soup w/Garden Vegetables●

Manischewitz - Borscht, Condensed Clear Chicken

Mixes From The Heartland ▲ -

Cajun Bean●

Cajun Pastalava●

Chicken Veggie●

Cowboy●

Green Chili Hamburger●

S

Green Chili Stew●
Hamburger Pasta●
Harvest Chicken N' Rice●
Italian Bean●
Minestrone●
Navy Bean●
Pasta Veggie●
Southwestern Chicken Stew●
Tex Mex Pasta●
Texas Sausage N' Bean●
Tortilla Pasta●

Orgran▲ - Cup Of Soup (Garden Vegetable, Sweet Corn, Tomato)

Pacific Natural Foods -
Cashew Carrot Ginger
Curried Red Lentil
Organic Creamy Butternut Squash
Organic Savory Chicken & Wild Rice
Organic Spicy (Black Bean w/Chicken Sausage, Chicken Fajita)

Progresso - Vegetable Classics (Garden Vegetable)

Safeway Select - Chicken w/Rice

Shelton's -
Black Bean & Chicken
Chicken Corn Chowder
Chicken Rice

Spartan Brand - Canned Beef Stew

Thai Kitchen - Soup Can (Coconut Ginger)

Wegmans Brand - Gazpacho

Spaghetti... see Pasta

Spaghetti Sauce... see Sauces

Spices... see Seasonings

S

Spinach... *All **Fresh** Spinach Is **Gluten/Casein/Soy Free***

Birds Eye - All Plain Frozen Spinach

C & W - All Plain Frozen Spinach

Cascadian Farms - Chopped, Organic Frozen Cut Spinach

Del Monte - All Plain Canned Spinach

Food Club Brand - Canned Cut Leaf

Freshlike - All Frozen Plain Spinach

Great Value Brand (Wal-Mart) - Canned Whole Leaf Spinach

Green Giant - Frozen Spinach No Sauce

Hannaford Brand - Whole Leaf

Hy-Vee - Canned, Frozen (Chopped, Leaf)

Laura Lynn - Canned

Lowes Foods Brand - Frozen (Chopped, Leaf)

Meijer Brand - Canned (Cut Leaf, No Salt, Regular), Frozen Spinach (Chopped, Leaf)

O Organics - Chopped, Frozen

Pictsweet - All Plain Frozen Spinach

Publix - Canned Spinach, Frozen (Chopped, Cut Leaf, Leaf)

Publix GreenWise Market - Organic (Baby Spinach Blend, Baby Spinach Salad, Spinach)

S&W - All Plain Canned Spinach

Safeway Brand - Canned Leaf, Frozen Chopped

Spartan Brand - Canned, Frozen (Chopped, Cut, Leaf)

Stop & Shop Brand - Chopped, Cut, Leaf, No Salt Added, Regular

Tasty Bite - Spinach Dal

Trader Joe's - All Plain Frozen Spinach

Wegmans Brand - Chopped Spinach (Frozen), Cut Leaf (Frozen), Whole Leaf

Winn Dixie - Canned (No Salt Added, Regular), Frozen (Chopped, Cut Leaf)

Woodstock Farms - Organic Frozen Cut Spinach

S Sports Drinks

    Gatorade - Propel Fitness Water (Berry, Black Cherry, Citrus, Grape, Kiwi Strawberry, Lemon, Mandarin Orange, Mango, Melon, Mixed Berry, Orange, Peach, Strawberry, Tropical Citrus)

    Powerade - Grape, Mountain Blast

    Wegmans Brand -

        MVP Sport Drink (Blue Freeze, Fruit Punch, Grape, Green Apple, Lemon Lime, Raspberry Lemonade)

        Velocity Fitness Water (Berry, Black Cherry, Grape, Kiwi Strawberry, Lemon)

Spread

    Bionaturae - Fruit Spread (All Varieties)

    Earth Balance - Natural Buttery Spread (Soy Free)

    Eden Organic - Butter (Apple, Cherry)

    Kalamata - Olive Spread

    Manischewitz - Apple Butter Spread

    Maple Grove Farms Of Vermont - Blended Maple, Honey Maple, Pure Maple

    Odell's - Clarified Butter, Popcorn Butter, Seafood Butter

    Purity Farms - Organic Ghee (Clarified Butter)

    Underwood Spreads - Deviled Ham

    Walden Farms - Spreads (Apple Butter, Apricot, Blueberry, Grape, Orange Marmalade, Raspberry, Strawberry)

Sprinkles... see Baking Decorations & Frostings

Squash... *All **Fresh** Squash Is **Gluten/Casein/Soy Free***

    Albertsons - Frozen

    C & W - All Plain Frozen Squash

    Cascadian Farms - Organic Frozen (Winter Squash)

    Meijer Brand - Frozen Squash (Cooked)

    Pictsweet - All Plain Frozen Squash

    Publix - Frozen (Cooked Squash, Yellow Sliced)

    Spartan Brand - Frozen Yellow

S

   Stop & Shop Brand
   Trader Joe's - All Plain Frozen Squash
   Winn Dixie - Frozen Yellow
Starch
   AgVantage Naturals▲ - Tapioca●
   Argo - Corn
   Authentic Foods▲ - Corn, Potato
   Bob's Red Mill▲ - Arrowroot, Corn, Potato
   El Peto▲ - Arrowroot, Corn, Potato, Tapioca
   Ener-G▲ - Potato
   Expandex▲ - Modified Tapioca Starch●
   Hodgson Mill▲ - Pure Corn
   Hy-Vee - Corn
   Kinnikinnick▲ - Corn, Potato, Tapioca
   Manischewitz - Potato
   Meijer Brand - Corn
   Safeway Brand - Corn
   Spartan Brand - Corn
   Winn Dixie
Steak ... *All Fresh Cut Meat Is Gluten/Casein/Soy Free
   (Non-Marinated, Unseasoned)*
Steak Sauce
   A-1
   Hannaford Brand
   Meijer Brand
   Publix
   Safeway Select - Bold, Original
   Spartan Brand - Original
   Wegmans Brand - Regular
   Winn & Lovett

S Stew... see also Soup
  Dinty Moore - Beef, Microwave Meals Beef Stew
Stir Fry Sauce
  Mr. Spice Organic - Ginger Stir Fry Sauce & Marinade
  Wegmans Brand - Sweet & Sour
Stir Fry Vegetables... see also Mixed Vegetables
  Albertsons - Stir Fry Vegetable Blend
  Cascadian Farm - Organic Frozen (Chinese Style, Thai Style)
  Meijer Brand - Frozen Vegetable Stir Fry
  Wegmans Brand - Asian, Cleaned And Cut Stir Fry Vegetables, Far
    East, Hong Kong
Stock
  Emeril's - Beef, Vegetable
  Full Flavor Foods▲ - Soup Stock Mix (Chicken●)
  Imagine - Organic (Beef, Beef Flavored Low Sodium, Chicken,
    Chicken Low Sodium, Vegetable)
  Kitchen Basics - Beef, Chicken, Clam, Ham, Pork, Seafood, Turkey,
    Unsalted (Beef, Chicken), Vegetable
  Wegmans Brand - Culinary Stock (Chicken, Thai, Vegetable)
  Winn Dixie - Resealable Boxes (Beef, Chicken, Vegetable)
Strawberries... *All Fresh Strawberries Are **Gluten/Casein/Soy Free***
  Albertsons - Frozen (Sliced w/Sugar, Whole)
  Cascadian Farm - Organic Frozen Strawberries
  Food Club Brand - Frozen
  Full Circle - Organic Whole Strawberries
  Great Value Brand (Wal-Mart) - Frozen (Sliced, Sliced w/Sugar, Whole)
  Hannaford Brand - Sliced (w/NutraSweet, w/Sugar, Whole)
  Hy-Vee - Frozen (Sliced, w/Sugar, Whole)
  Kroger Brand - Plain Frozen Fruit
  Meijer Brand - Frozen (Organic, Sliced), Whole Individually Quick Frozen
  Publix - Frozen (Sliced, Sweetened, Whole)

S

Safeway Brand - Frozen (Sliced w/Sugar, Sliced w/Sweetener, Whole)

Spartan Brand - Sliced, Whole

Stop & Shop Brand - Sliced Strawberries (In Sugar, Regular), Whole

Trader Joe's - Frozen

Wegmans Brand - Frozen Sliced w/Sugar

Winn Dixie - Frozen (Sugar Whole, Whole)

Woodstock Farms - Organic Frozen Whole Strawberries

Stuffing

Deerfields Bakery▲ - Stuffing Cubes

El Peto▲ - Stuffing

Succotash...*All **Fresh** Succotash Is **Gluten/Casein/Soy Free***

Publix - Frozen Vegetable Blend

Spartan Brand - Frozen

Winn Dixie - Frozen Yellow

Sugar

Albertsons - Granulated, Light Brown, Powdered

Diamond Falls - Brown, Granulated, Powdered

Domino - Confectioners, Cubes, Dark Brown, Granulated, Light Brown, Pure Cane

Food Club Brand - Granulated, Light Brown, Powdered

Full Circle - Organic Cane Sugar

Hannaford Brand - Dark Brown, Granulated, Light Brown, Powdered

Home Harvest Brand - Confectioners Powdered, Dark Brown, Granulated, Light Brown

Hy-Vee - Confectioners Powdered, Dark Brown, Light Brown, Pure Cane

Kroger Brand - Dark Brown, Granulated, Light Brown, Powdered

Laura Lynn - Brown, Confectioners, White

Lowes Foods Brand - Granulated, Light Brown, Powdered

Meijer Brand - Confectioners, Dark Brown, Granulated, Light Brown

Midwest Country Fare - Granulated, Light Brown, Powdered

S   O Organics

Publix - Granulated, Dark Brown, Light Brown, Powdered

Safeway Brand - Brown (Dark, Light), Granulated, Powdered

Spartan Brand - Confectioners Powdered, Granulated, Light Brown

Stop & Shop Brand - Granulated

Tops - Light Brown

Wegmans Brand - Cocktail Sugar (Cosmopolitan, Lemon, Mandarin), Dark Brown, Granulated White, Light Brown

Winn Dixie - Granulated, Light Brown, Powdered

Woodstock Farms - Organic Sugar (Brown, Powdered, Pure Cane, Turbinado)

Sugar Substitute/Sweetener

Albertsons - Aspartame, Saccharin

Equal

Great Value Brand (Wal-Mart) - Calorie Free Sweetener

Hannaford Brand - Sweetener (Aspartame, Sweet Choice)

Hy-Vee - Aspartame Sweetener

NutraSweet - Original

Spartan Brand

Splenda - Brown Sugar Blend, Café Sticks, Flavors For Coffee (French Vanilla, Hazelnut, Mocha), No Calorie Sweetener (Granulated), Sugar Blend

Sweet and Low

Sweet Fiber - All Natural Sweeter●

Wegmans Brand - Sugar Substitute w/Saccharin

Wholesome Sweeteners - All Varieties *(Except Organic Light Corn Syrup)*

Winn Dixie - Sweetener w/Aspartame

Sunflower Seeds... see Seeds

Sweet & Sour Sauce

LaChoy - Regular, Sweet & Sour Duck Sauce

Mr. Spice Organic - Sweet & Sour Sauce & Marinade

Wegmans

S

Sweet Potatoes... *All **Fresh** Sweet Potatoes Are **Gluten/Casein/ Soy Free***

   Meijer Brand - Cut (Light Syrup)

Sweetener... see Sugar Substitute/Sweetener

Swiss Chard... *All **Fresh** Swiss Chard Is **Gluten/Casein/Soy Free***

Swordfish... see also Fish... *All **Fresh** Fish Is **Gluten/Casein/Soy Free** (Non-Marinated, Unseasoned)*

   Full Circle - All Natural Swordfish Steaks

   Wegmans - Swordfish

   Whole Catch - Fillet

Syrup

   Beehive - Corn Syrup

   Cabot - Vermont Pure Maple Syrup

   Crown - Corn Syrup

   Golden Griddle - Original Syrup

   Grand Selections - 100% Pure Maple

   Hannaford Brand - Pancake (2% Maple, Lite)

   Hershey's - Chocolate Syrup (Lite, Regular, w/Calcium)

   Hy-Vee - Butter Flavor, Chocolate, Lite, Pancake & Waffle, Strawberry

   Karo - Corn Syrup w/Brown Sugar, Dark Corn, Lite Corn, Pancake Syrup

   Lily White - Corn Syrup

   Log Cabin - Butter Flavored, Lite, Original, Sugar Free

   Lundberg▲ - Sweet Dreams Brown Rice Syrup (Eco Farmed, Organic)

   Maple Grove Farms Of Vermont -

      Flavored Syrups (Apricot, Blueberry, Boysenberry, Raspberry, Strawberry)

      Pure & Organic Maple Syrup

      Sugar Free Syrup (Maple Flavor, Vermont)

   Meijer Brand - Butter, Chocolate, Lite Butter, Lite, Lite Corn, Regular)

   Midwest Country Fare - Pancake & Waffle (Butter, Original)

S

Mrs. Renfro's - Cane, Country

Nescafe - Ice Java Coffee Syrup (Cappuccino Fat Free, Chocolate Mocha, French Vanilla Café Fat Free)

O Organics - 100% Pure Maple

Old Tyme - Original, No Sugar Added

Organic Nectars - Chocagave, Vanillagave

Publix - Butter Maple (Lite, Regular), Chocolate (Regular, Sugar Free), Pancake (Lite, Regular)

Safeway Brand - Butter Light, Chocolate, Light, Old Fashioned

Smucker's -

Fruit Syrup (Blackberry, Blueberry, Boysenberry, Red Raspberry, Strawberry)

Sugar Free Breakfast Syrup

Spartan Brand - 2% Real Maple, Artificial Butter, Corn Syrup, Reduced Calorie (Butter, Lite)

Uncle Luke's - 100% Pure Maple Syrup

Vermont Maid - Butter Lite, Original

Walden Farms -

Fruit Syrups (Blueberry, Strawberry)

Single Serve Packets (Chocolate, Pancake)

Syrup (Chocolate, Pancake)

Wegmans Brand -

Butter Flavor (Light)

Chocolate Flavored

Pancake (Light, Regular)

Pure Maple (Organic Dark Amber, Regular)

Sugar Free

Winn & Lovett - 100% Pure Maple (Dark, Medium), Blackberry, Blueberry, Maple Praline Sugar Free, Raspberry

Winn Dixie - Butter Flavor, Chocolate, Lite, Regular, Strawberry

T

Taco Sauce
  Chi-Chi's - Taco Sauce
  Frontera - Taco Sauce (Chipotle Garlic, Roasted Tomato)
  Hy-Vee - Medium, Mild
  La Victoria - Green (Medium, Mild), Red (Medium, Mild)
  Old El Paso - Hot, Medium, Mild
  Ortega - Original (Hot, Medium, Mild)
  Safeway Brand
  Spartan Brand - Fat Free (Medium, Mild)
Taco Seasoning... see also Seasonings
  Chi-Chi's - Fiesta Restaurante Seasoning Mix
  Ortega - Chipotle Mix, Jalapeno & Onion Mix, Taco Seasoning Mix
Taco Shells
  Hy-Vee - White Corn Tortilla
  Old El Paso -
    Stand 'N Stuff Yellow Corn Taco Shells
    Taco Shells (Super Stuffer, White Corn, Yellow Corn)
    Tostada Shells
  Safeway Brand - Taco Shells (Jumbo, White Corn)
  Taco Bell - Taco Shells (12 ct, 18 ct)
  Winn Dixie - White Corn
Tahini
  Arrowhead Mills - Organic Sesame Tahini
  MaraNatha - Natural w/Salt (Raw, Roasted)
  Woodstock Farms - Organic Sesame Tahini (Unsalted)
Tamales
  Amy's - Black Bean Verde, Roasted Vegetable
Tangerines... *All **Fresh** Tangerines Are **Gluten/Casein/Soy Free***

T **Tapioca**
   Let's Do...Organic - Organic (Granules, Pearls, Starch)
Taquitos
   Delimex - Chicken Taquitos (12 ct., 25 ct., 36 ct., Costco 66 ct.)
   El Monterey - Taquitos Corn Tortillas (Chicken, Shredded Steak)
Tartar Sauce
   McCormick - Fat Free
Tarts
   Crave Bakery▲ - Lemon, Pumpkin
Tater Tots... see Potatoes
Tea
   Arizona -
      50% Juice & Decaf Tea (Apple Green, Pomegranate Green)
      Arnold Palmer's Lite (Green Tea Lemonade, Half & Half Iced Tea
         Lemonade)
      Blueberry Tea (Green, White)
      Decaf Diet w/Ginseng
      Diet
         Peach Iced Tea
         Iced Tea w/(Raspberry Flavor, White Cranberry Apple Green)
      Energy Drinks Green Tea (Diet, Regular)
      Green Tea (Diet, Regular, w/Ginger)
      Green Tea w/Ginseng
      Half & Half (Iced Tea/Lemonade, Lite Green Tea/Lemonade)
      Iced Teas
         Sun Brewed, w/(Ginseng Extract, Lemon Flavor)
      No Caffeine Herbal
      Plum Green Tea
      Peach Green Tea
      White Cranberry/Apple Green Tea (Diet, Regular)

Bigelow Tea -

American Classical Tea (Charleston Breakfast, Governor Gray, Plantation Peach Tree, Regular, Rockville Raspberry)

Chinese Oolong

Darjeeling

Decaffeinated

Constant Comment

Earl Grey

English Teatime

Green Tea

Earl Grey

English Breakfast

English Teatime

Flavored Tea

Cinnamon Stick

Eggnogg'n Tea

Plantation Mint

Raspberry Royale

Green Tea

Constant Comment Green

Earl Grey Green

Green Tea w/(Chinese Oolong, Jasmine, Mint)

Regular

Herbal Tea

Berri Good

Blueberry

Cozy Chamomile

Mint Medley

Peppermint

Sweet Dreams

Tasty Tangerine

T

Loose Tea
- Constant Comment
- Earl Grey
- English Breakfast
- Green

Organic
- Green Tea w/Pomegranate & Acai
- Rooibos w/Asian Pear
- White Tea w/Raspberry & Chrysanthemum

Celestial Seasonings -

African Rooibos Tea
- Madagascar Vanilla Red
- Moroccan Pomegranate Red
- Peach Apricot Honeybush

Black Teas
- Morning Thunder
- Organic Black
- Tuscany Orange Spice

Chai
- Chocolate Caramel Enchantment
- Decaf India Spice
- Decaf Sweet Coconut Thai
- India Spice

Cool Brew Iced Tea
- Peach Ice
- Raspberry Ice

Green Tea
- Decaf Lemon Myrtle Organic
- Organic Green
- Tropical Acai Berry

Herbal Tea
   Acai Mango Zinger
   Bengal Spice
   Caffeine Free
   Chamomile
   Mint Magic
   Peppermint
   Red Zinger
   Sleepytime (Regular, Vanilla)
   Sweet Clementine Chamomile Organic
Holiday Tea
   Candy Cane Lane
   Nutcracker Sweet
White Tea
   Vanilla Apple White Organic

Gold Peak - Iced Tea (Diet, Green Sweetened, Lemon, Sweetened, Unsweetened)

Hannaford Brand - Instant Iced Tea w/Lemon, Orange Pekoe Bags (Decaf, Regular)

Hansen's - All Varieties

Honest Tea - Assam Black, Black Forest Berry, Community Green, Green Dragon, Honey Green, Jasmine Green Energy, Just Black, Just Green, Lemon Black, Lori's Lemon, Mango Acai, Mango Green, Moroccan Mint Green, Peach Oolalong, Peach White, Pearfect White, Pomegranate Red, Pomegranate White

Hy-Vee - Decaf (Green, Tea Bags), Family Size Tea Bags, Green Tea Bags, Instant, Orange & Spice Specialty

Inko's White Tea - Apricot, Blueberry, Cherry Vanilla, Energy, Honeydew, Lemon, Lychee, Original, Unsweetened Hint O'Mint, Unsweetened Honeysuckle, Unsweetened Original, White Peach

Kettle Brewed - Unsweetened Green & White Tea

T Lipton -
- Diet Ice Tea Mix (Lemon (Decaf, Regular), Peach, Raspberry)
- Regular
  - Calorie Free Ice Tea Mix (Lemon)
  - Green Tea Bags (100% Natural, Regular)
  - Instant Ice Tea (100% Instant & Decaf)

Meijer Brand - Instant, Tea Bags (Decaf, Green, Green Decaf, Regular)

Nestea - Iced Tea Mix (Lemon, Lemonade Flavor), Unsweetened (Decaf, Regular)

Newman's Own - Lemonade Iced Tea

Numi - Aged Earl Grey, Golden Chai, Golden Chai, Honeybush, Jasmine Green, Mate Lemon Green

Oregon Chai -
- Chai Tea Latte Concentrate
  - Caffeine Free Original
  - Matcha Green Tea
  - Peppermint Original
  - Slightly Sweet Original
  - Sugar Free Original
  - The Original
  - Vanilla
  - Vegan Original

Pacific Natural Foods - Organic Iced Tea (Green, Lemon, Peach, Raspberry, Sweetened Black)

Prairie Farms - Sweetened Iced Tea

Publix -
- Iced Tea (Sweetened, Unsweetened)
- Instant (Lemon, Regular)

Red Rose - All Varieties

Republic Of Tea - All Varieties●

Rishi Tea - All Varieties

Safeway Brand - Iced Tea Mix (All Flavors)

Safeway Select - Chai Tea, Earl Gray, Herbal Tea (Chamomile, Evening Delight, Lemon, Peppermint), Quiet Morning, Specialty Tea, Tea (Black, Green, Orange Spice)

Salada Tea - All Varieties

Snapple - All Tea

SoBe - Green

Spartan Brand - Orange Pekoe (Decaf, Regular), Green, Instant

Stash Tea - All Varieties *(Except Ginger Teas)*

Tazo Tea - In Bags (Awake, Calm, Organic Chai, Passion, Wild Sweet Orange

Wegmans Brand -

  Black Tea

  Decaf (Black Tea, Green Tea)

  Earl Grey (Black, Black Decaf, Green, Supreme)

  English Breakfast (Black, Organic)

  Green Tea

  Iced Tea Lemon

  Iced Tea Mix (Decaf, Regular, w/Natural Lemon Flavor & Sugar (Decaf, Regular))

  Organic (Chai, Chamomile, Earl Grey, English Breakfast, Jasmine Green, Peppermint, Rooibos Strawberry Cream)

  Sencha (Pure Japanese Green)

  Winn Dixie - Regular & Family (Decaffeinated, Tea Bags)

Teff

  Bob's Red Mill▲ - Flour, Whole Grain Teff

  Shiloh Farms - Brown, Ivory

Tequila... *All **Distilled** Alcohol Is **Gluten/Casein/Soy Free** [2]*

Tilapia... see Fish... *All **Fresh** Fish Is **Gluten/Casein/Soy Free** (Non-Marinated, Unseasoned)*

Tomatillos... *All **Fresh** Tomatillos Are **Gluten/Casein/Soy Free***

  Las Palmas - Crushed Tomatillos

T Tomato Juice... see Drinks/Juice

Tomato Paste

   Albertsons - Regular

   Contadina - Tomato Paste

   Del Monte - Organic Tomato Paste

   Hannaford Brand

   Hy-Vee - Regular Tomato

   Meijer Brand - Domestic, Organic

   Muir Glen - Organic

   Publix

   S&W

   Spartan Brand - 26% Tomato

   Wegmans Brand

   Woodstock Farms - Organic

Tomato Puree

   Contadina

   Dei Fratelli

   Hunt's

   Meijer Brand

   Muir Glen - Organic

   S&W

   Wegmans Brand

Tomato Sauce... see Sauces

Tomatoes... *All **Fresh** Tomatoes Are **Gluten/Casein/Soy Free***

   Albertsons - Canned, Celery & Bell Peppers, Diced Tomatoes &
     Green Chilies, Diced w/Jalapenos, Stewed (Italian, w/Onions),
     Whole (No Salt, Regular)

   Contadina -
     Crushed w/(Italian Herbs, Regular, Roasted Garlic)
     Diced (Petite Cut, Regular)

Diced w/(Italian Herbs, Roasted Garlic, Roasted Red Pepper, Zucchini Bell Pepper & Carrots)

Stewed w/(Italian Herbs, Onions Celery & Green Peppers)

Dei Fratelli -

Canned

Chopped (Italian, Mexican, w/Onion & Garlic)

Crushed (Regular, w/Basil & Herbs)

Diced (In Hearty Sauce, Low Sodium, Seasoned)

No Salt Whole

Petite Diced (Regular, w/Onion & Celery & Pepper)

Stewed

Whole (In Puree, Regular)

Del Monte -

Diced

Tomatoes Pasta Style

Tomatoes w/Basil, Garlic & Oregano

Tomatoes w/Green Pepper & Onion

Tomatoes w/Mushrooms & Garlic

Tomatoes w/Zesty Mild Green Chiles

Garden Select

Petite Diced Tomatoes

Sliced Tomatoes

Organic Crushed Tomatoes

Petite Cut

Tomatoes

Tomatoes w/Garlic & Olive Oil

Tomatoes w/Zesty Jalapenos

Stewed Tomatoes (Italian Recipe, No Salt Added, Original Recipe)

Tomato Sauce

Regular

No Salt Added

T

Eden Organic -
  Crushed (Regular, w/Basil, w/Onion & Garlic)
  Diced (Regular, w/Basil, w/Chilies, w/Green Chilies, w/Roasted
    Onion)
  Whole Tomatoes (w/Basil, Regular)

Hannaford Brand -
  Crushed (In Puree, Regular)
  Diced (Regular, No Salt, w/Green Chilies, w/Roasted Garlic &
    Onion)
  Puree
  Stewed (Italian, Mexican, No Salt, Regular)
  Whole Peeled

Hunt's -
  Crushed
  Diced (Fire Roasted, Fire Roasted w/Garlic, Petite, Regular,
    w/Balsamic Vinegar Basil & Oil, w/Basil Garlic & Oregano,
    w/Green Pepper Celery & Onions, w/Roasted Garlic, w/Sweet
    Onions)
  Organic Diced
  Petite Diced
  Paste (Basil Garlic & Oregano, Regular)
  Puree
  Stewed (No Salt Added, Regular)
  Whole (Basil, No Salt Added, Regular)

Hy-Vee - Diced (Chili Ready, Regular, w/Garlic & Onion), Italian Style
  Stewed, Original Diced & Green Chilies, Petite Diced (Regular,
  w/Garlic & Olive Oil, w/Sweet Onion), Stewed, Tomato Paste,
  Whole Peeled

Meijer Brand - Crushed In Puree, Diced (Chili Ready, Green Chilies, In
  Italian, In Juice, Organic, Petite), Stewed (Italian, Mexican, Regular),
  Whole (Organic, Peeled, Peeled No Salt, w/Basil Organic)

Midwest Country Fair - Diced, Stewed, Whole Peeled

Muir Glen - Organic (Crushed (Fire Roasted, w/Basil), Diced (Fire Roasted, No Salt Added, Regular, w/Basil & Garlic, w/Garlic & Onion, w/Green Chilies, w/Italian Herbs), Stewed, Whole (Fire Roasted, Peeled, Peeled Plum, Peeled w/Basil))

Publix - Crushed, Diced, Diced No Salt, Diced w/Green Chilies, Diced w/Roasted Garlic & Onion, Paste, Peeled Whole, Pureed, Sauce, Sliced & Stewed

Publix GreenWise Market - Organic (Crushed, Diced, Diced w/Basil Garlic & Oregano, Fancy Sliced, Fancy Sliced Italian, Paste, Pureed, Sauce)

S&W - All Canned Tomatoes

Safeway Brand - Crushed, Diced (Fire Roasted, Peeled, Peeled No Salt, Petite), Italian Style Stewed, Mexican Style Stewed, Whole Peeled

Spartan Brand - Diced (For Chili, Mexican, Regular, w/Green Chilies, w/Roasted Garlic & Onions), Italian Stewed, Specialty Crushed, Whole

Wegmans Brand -

Coarse Ground

Crushed (w/Italian, Style Herbs, Regular)

Diced (Chili Style, Italian Style, Petite, Regular, Roasted Garlic & Onion)

Italian Classics San Marzano Tomatoes Whole Peeled

Italian Style (Diced Tomatoes, Stewed, Whole w/Basil)

Kitchen Cut w/Basil

Organic (Diced, Diced In Juice)

Peeled Whole

Petite Diced Tomatoes w/Garlic Olive Oil & Seasoning

Puree

Stewed

Whole Peeled

Winn Dixie - Canned (Crushed, Diced, Diced w/Chilies, Italian Style (Diced, Stewed), Paste, Petite Diced, Petite Diced w/Onion Celery Green Peppers, Puree, Sauce, Stewed, Whole Peeled)

T Woodstock Farms -
    Organic
        Crushed (Basil, Original)
        Diced (Basil & Garlic, Italian Herbs, No Salt, Original)
        Paste
        Tomato Sauce (No Salt Added, Original)
        Whole Peeled (In Juice, w/Basil)

Tonic... see Soda Pop/Carbonated Beverages

Toppings... see Baking Decorations & Frostings

Tortilla Chips... see Chips

Tortilla Soup... see Soup

Tortillas
  Food For Life - Brown Rice, Sprouted Organic Corn
  French Meadow Bakery - Gluten Free Tortillas●
  Mission -
    Corn Tortillas
      Extra Thin
      Super Size White
      Super Size Yellow
      White
      Yellow
  Que Pasa - Corn Tortillas

Trail Mix... see also Nuts
  Eden Organic - All Mixed Up
  Enjoy Life▲ - Not Nuts! (Beach Bash●, Mountain Mambo●)
  Frito Lay - Nut & Fruit
  Hy-Vee - Berry, Raisin & Nut, Tropical
  Mareblu Naturals -
    Crunch (Almond, Almond Coconut, Cashew, Cashew Coconut, CranMango Cashew, Pecan Cinnamon, Pistachio)

Trail Mix Crunch (Blueberry Pomegranate, Cranberry Pomegranate, Cranblueberry Trail, Cranstrawberry Trail, Pecan Trail, Pistachio Trail)

Nonuttin' Foods▲ - Energy Explosion Trail Mix

Oskri Organics - Almond Honey Crunch, Cashew Honey Crunch w/Cranberries, Pecan Honey Crunch w/Cinnamon

Winn Dixie - Energy Snack Trail Mix

Trek Mix... see Trail Mix

Tuna... see also Fish... *All Fresh Fish Is Gluten/Casein/Soy Free (Non-Marinated, Unseasoned)*

Bumble Bee -

Chunk Light Solid White Albacore In Water

Prime Fillet Solid Light Tuna Tonno In Olive Oil

Prime Fillet Solid White Albacore In (Very Low Sodium In Water, Water)

Solid White Albacore In Water

Crown Prince Natural - Solid White Albacore Tuna (No Salt Added Packed In Spring Water, Packed In Spring Water)

Full Circle - All Natural Yellowfin Tuna Steaks

Member's Mark - Highest Quality Solid White Albacore Tuna In Water

Publix - Tuna Fillets

Starkist

Gourmet Choice Solid Light Tuna Fillet In (Olive Oil, Water)

Low Sodium Chunk Light In Water

Wegmans Brand - Yellowfin Light In Water

Turkey... see also Deli Meat ... *All Fresh Meat Is Gluten/Casein/Soy Free (Non-Marinated, Unseasoned)*

Applegate Farms -

Organic (Herb Turkey Breast, Roasted Turkey Breast, Smoked Turkey Breast)

Organic Turkey Burgers

Organic Uncured Turkey Hot Dogs

T

    Natural (Herb Turkey Breast, Honey & Maple Turkey Breast, Roasted Turkey, Smoked Turkey Breast, Turkey Bologna, Turkey Salami)

    Natural Uncured Turkey Hot Dogs

Butterball -

    All Natural Turkey (Cutlets, Filets, Strips, Tenders)

    Fresh Li'l Butterball Turkey *(Except Gravy Packet w/Wheat Flour)*

    Fresh Whole Turkey *(Except Gravy Packet w/Wheat Flour)*

    Frozen Fully Cooked Li'l Butterball Baked Turkey *(Except Gravy Packet w/Wheat Flour)*

    Frozen Fully Cooked Turkey (Baked, Smoked) *(Except Gravy Packet w/Wheat Flour)*

    Frozen Li'l Butterball *(Except Gravy Packet w/Wheat Flour)*

    Frozen Whole Turkey *(Except Stuffed Turkeys & Gravy Packet w/ Wheat Flour)*

    Ground Turkey (Italian Style, Regular, Seasoned, White)

    Turkey (Drumsticks, Thighs, Wings)

    Turkey Bacon (Lower Sodium, Regular, Thin & Crispy)

    Turkey Breasts (Fresh, Frozen)

    Turkey Burgers (All Natural, Seasoned)

    Turkey Sausage (Fresh Bratwurst, Fresh Breakfast, Fresh Hot Italian, Fresh Sweet Italian)

Dietz & Watson -

    Black Forest Turkey

    Fire Roasted Breast Of Turkey

    Glazed Honey Cured Turkey Breast

    Italian Turkey

    Maple & Honey Cured Turkey Breast

    Mesquite Turkey Breast

    Oven Classic Turkey Breast

    Smoked Peppercorn Turkey Breast

Empire Kosher - Ground Turkey (Fresh, Frozen)

Garrett County Farms -

Frozen Turkey Maple Breakfast Links

Turkey Andouille

Turkey Breast (Pan Roasted, Sliced (Roasted, Smoked, Turkey Ham, Turkey Ham Steak), Smoked)

Turkey Franks

Turkey Kielbasa

Turkey Tom Tom Snack Sticks

Honeysuckle White -

Estate Recipe Turkey Deli Meat

    Buffalo Style

    Canadian Brand Maple

    Dry Roasted

    Hickory Smoked (Honey Pepper, Original)

    Honey Smoked

    Mesquite Smoked

Fresh

    Breast (Bone In, Cutlets, Roast, Strips, Tenderloins, Thin Cut Slices)

    Drumsticks

    Neck Pieces

    Split Breast

    Thighs

    Wings (Drumettes, Portions, Regular)

Frozen (Boneless Turkey w/Gravy, Turkey Burgers)

Fully Cooked Hickory Smoked Bone In Turkey Breast

Ground Turkey

    All (85/15, 93/7, 97% Fat Free, 99% Fat Free, Italian Style Seasoned, Patties, Roll, Taco Seasoned, Value Pack)

Hardwood Smoked Bacon

Hardwood Smoked Franks

T

Hickory Smoked Cooked Turkey Salami

Hickory Smoked Turkey Ham

Hickory Smoked Turkey Pastrami

Lunch Meat Deli Sliced

    Hickory Smoked (Honey Turkey Breast, Turkey Breast)

    Oven Roasted Turkey Breast

    Turkey Pastrami

Marinated Turkey Selections

    Creamy Dijon Mustard Breast Tenderloins

    Italian Herb Rotisserie Boneless Breast Roast

    Lemon Garlic Breast Tenderloins

    Original Style Rotisserie Boneless Breast Roast

    Rotisserie Breast Tenderloins

    Zesty Italian Herb Breast Tenderloins

Sausage

    Bratwurst

    Links (Breakfast, Hot Italian, Original Smoked, Poblano Pepper, Sweet Italian)

    Patties

    Roll (Breakfast, Mild Italian)

Simply Done Whole Young (Turkey, Turkey Breast)

Turkey Bologna

Turkey Breast Deli Meats

    Cajun Style Hickory Smoked

    Golden Roasted

    Hickory (Smoked, Smoked Peppered)

    Honey Mesquite Smoked

    Oven Prepared

Whole Young Turkeys

    All Natural

    Cajun Style

Fresh

Frozen

Fully Cooked (Hickory Smoked, Oven Roasted)

Honey Roasted

Hormel -

Deli Sliced (Oven Roasted, Smoked)

Chunk Meats Turkey

Natural Choice Deli Oven Roasted

Hy-Vee -

Deli Thin Sliced Turkey Breast (Honey Roasted, Oven Roasted)

Thin Sliced (Honey Turkey, Turkey)

Isaly's - Oven Roasted Breast Of Turkey

Jennie-O Turkey Store -

Fresh

Extra Lean Boneless Turkey Breast Tenderloins

Extra Lean Turkey Breast Cutlets

Breakfast Sausage (Mild Links, Mild Patties)

Dinner Sausage (Hot Italian, Lean Turkey Bratwurst, Sweet Italian)

Ground Turkey (Extra Lean, Lean, Regular)

Grand Champion Turkey Breast (Hickory Smoked, Honey Cured, Mesquite Smoked, Oven Roasted)

Natural Choice Deli Counter Turkey Breast (Applewood Smoked, Honey Roasted, Peppered)

Premium Fresh Deli Counter Turkey Breast (Golden Classic Herb Roasted, Hickory Smoked Honey Roasted, Honey Cured, Mesquite Smoked, Oven Roasted)

Premium Seasoned Deli Counter Turkey Breast (Bourbon Maple, Cajun Style, Cracked Pepper, Sun Dried Tomato, Sweet Maple)

Kayem - Turkey Breast Homestyle

T Meijer Brand -

Gold Turkey (Hen, Tom)

Hen Turkey

Frozen (Breast Tenders, Duckling, Giblets, Split Breast, Young)

Regular Turkey Breast

Tom Turkey

Turkey Basted w/Timer

Turkey Breast (Fresh, Fresh Natural, Honey Roasted, Oven Roasted, Smoked)

Organic Prairie -

Fresh Organic

Sliced Roast Turkey Breast 6 oz.

Sliced Smoked Turkey Breast 6 oz.

Frozen Organic

Ground Turkey 12 oz.

Whole Young Turkey (10-14 lbs.), (14-18 lbs.)

Oscar Mayer -

Deli Fresh Meats (Oven Roasted (98% Fat Free Turkey, Turkey Breast), Smoked Turkey Breast) Shaved Deli Fresh Meats (Cracked Black Peppered Turkey Breast, Honey Smoked Turkey Breast, Oven Roasted Turkey Breast, Smoked Turkey Breast)

Thin Sliced Deli Fresh (Honey Smoked Turkey Breast, Oven Roasted Turkey Breast, Smoked Turkey Breast)

Publix -

Deli Fully Cooked Turkey (Breast, Whole)

Deli Pre Pack Lunch Meats (Extra Thin Sliced Oven Roasted Turkey Breast, Extra Thin Sliced Smoked Turkey Breast, Smoked Turkey, Turkey Breast)

Fresh Young Turkey (Breast, Whole)

Shelton's - Free Range Ground Turkey (#1 Chub Pack, #3 Chub Pack), Free Range Ground White Turkey (#1 Chub Pack), Free Range Whole Turkey (8-15 lbs., 16-26 lbs.), Organic (Large, Whole Small), Turkey Burgers

T

SPAM - Classic, Less Sodium, Lite, Oven Roasted Turkey, Smoked Flavored

Valley Fresh - 100% Natural Premium White Turkey

Wegmans Brand -

Lean Ground Turkey (94%, 99%)

Organic Turkey Breast (Honey Roasted, Oven Roasted)

Sliced Turkey Breast (Hickory Smoked, Oven Browned)

Split Turkey Breast

Thin Sliced Turkey Breast Cutlets

Turkey (Breast Tenders, Drumsticks, London Broil, Thighs, Wings)

Wellshire Farms -

All Natural Turkey Breast (Pan Roasted, Smoked)

Morning Maple Turkey Breakfast Link Sausage

Sliced (Oven Roasted Turkey Breast, Smoked Turkey Breast, Turkey Bologna, Turkey Ham)

Turkey (Andouille Sausage, Franks, Kielbasa)

Turkey Dinner Link Sausage Mild Italian Style

Turkey Ham (Ham Steak, Nuggets, Whole)

Turkey Tom Toms (Hot & Spicy, Original)

Wellshire Organic - Organic Turkey (Andouille, Bacon, Franks, Kielbasa)

Winn Dixie - Thin Sliced Turkey (Oven Roasted, Smoked, Smoked Honey)

Turkey Bacon... see Bacon

Turkey Breast... see Turkey

Turkey Burgers... see Burgers... see Turkey

Turkey Ham... see also Ham... see also Turkey

Honeysuckle White - Hickory Smoked Turkey Ham

Jennie-O Turkey Store - Extra Lean, Lean

Perdue - Deli Turkey Ham Hickory Smoked

Wellshire Farms - Turkey Ham (Ham Steak, Nuggets, Whole)

Turkey Jerky... see Jerky/Beef Sticks

T

Turkey Lunch Meat... see Deli Meat

U

Turnips... *All Fresh Turnips Are **Gluten/Casein/Soy Free***

V

   C & W - All Plain Frozen Turnips

   Pictsweet - All Plain Frozen Turnips

   Safeway Brand - Frozen Chopped

   Winn Dixie - Frozen Chopped

U

V

Vanilla Extract... see Extract

Vanilla Powder

   Authentic Foods ▲

Vegetable Juice... see Juice/Drinks

Vinegar

   Albertsons - Apple Cider, Red Wine, White Distilled

   Bakers & Chefs - White Distilled

   Bionaturae - Balsamic

   Bragg - Organic Apple Cider

   Di Lusso - Red Wine

   Eden Organic - Organic (Apple Cider, Brown Rice, Red Wine, Ume Plum)

   Food Club Brand - Cider, White

   Full Circle - Organic Balsamic Vinegar

   Grand Selections - Balsamic Of Modena, Red Wine, White Wine

   Great Value Brand (Wal-Mart) - Apple Cider, Distilled White

   Hannaford Brand - Appled Cider, Red Wine, White

   Heinz - Apple Cider, Distilled White, Garlic Wine, Red Wine

   Holland House - All Vinegars *(Except Malt Vinegar)*

   Home Harvest Brand - White

   Hy-Vee - Apple Cider Flavored Distilled, White Distilled

V

W

Lowes Foods Brand - Cider, White

Meijer Brand - Balsamic Aged (4 Yr, 12 Yr), Cider, Red Wine, White Distilled, White Wine

Musselman's - Apple Cider, White Distilled

Newman's Own Organics - Balsamic

Marukan - Rice Wine Vinegar

Nishiki - Sushi Vinegar

O Organics - Balsamic

Publix - Apple Cider, Balsamic, Red Wine, White Distilled

Regina - Fine (Balsamic, Red Wine, White Wine), Raspberry Balsamic

Safeway Select - Apple Cider, Distilled, Red Wine, Rice, White Wine

Spartan Brand - Cider, White

Spectrum - Balsamic, Organic (Balsamic, Brown Rice, Distilled White, Filtered Apple Cider, Golden Balsamic, Red Wine, Seasoned Brown Rice, Unfiltered Apple Cider, White Wine)

Wegmans Brand - Apple Cider, Asian Classic Rice Vinegar, Chianti Red Wine, Italian Classic Balsamic Vinegar Of Modena (Four Leaf, Three Leaf, Two Leaf), Red Wine, Tuscan White Wine, White Distilled

Winn Dixie - Apple Cider, White

Vitamins... see Gluten/Casein/Soy Free OTC Pharmacy Section

Vodka... *All Distilled Alcohol Is Gluten/Casein/Soy Free* [2]

W

Waffles/Waffle Mix... see Pancakes/Pancake Mix

Walnuts... see Nuts

Wasabi

Eden - Wasabi Powder

Dietz & Watson - Wasabi Mustard

Hime - Powdered Sushi Wasabi

Sushi Sonic - Real Wasabi

W **Water**

Aquafina -

Flavor Splash (Grape, Lemon, Peach Mango, Raspberry, Strawberry Kiwi, Wild Berry)

Purified Drinking Water

Sparkling (Lemon Lime, Original)

Crystal Geyser - Alpine Spring

Dasani - Essence (Black Cherry, Lime, Strawberry Kiwi), Purified

Deja Blue - Purified Drinking Water

Evian

Fiji - Natural Artesian

Food Club Brand - Distilled, Drinking, Spring

Hannaford Brand - Sparkling (Black Cherry, Key Lime, Kiwi Strawberry, Peach, Raspberry, Tropical Punch, White Grape)

Hy-Vee - 10 oz. Fun Pack (Flavored, Regular), Mother's Choice Infant Water w/Fluoride, Natural Spring, Premium Distilled, Purified, Spring, Tonic

Ice Mountain

Lowes Foods Brand - Distilled, Drinking, Spring

Meijer Brand - Calcium, Distilled, Natural Calcium, Spring

Poland Spring - Sparkling Spring

Publix - Spring Water

Safeway Brand - Drinking, Purified Drinking, Spring

San Pellegrino - Sparkling Water

Spartan Brand - Water (Distilled, Drinking, Natural Spring, Spring)

Sweet Bay - Distilled, Drinking Water w/Minerals, Natural Spring Water Sodium Free

Wegmans Brand -

Aqua V Vitamin Infused Lemonade

Sparkling Water (Berry, FYFGA Natural, Lemon, Lime, Mineral, Mixed Berry, Orange, Raspberry, Tangerine Lime)

Spring (Regular, w/Fluoride)

Winn Dixie - Distilled, Drinking, Purified, Spring

Water Chestnuts... **All Fresh Water Chestnuts Are Gluten/Casein/ Soy Free*

   Reese - Diced, Sliced, Whole

   Spartan Brand - Canned

Watermelon... **All Fresh Watermelon Is Gluten/Casein/Soy Free*

Whipping Cream

   Soyatoo - Rice Whip

Whiskey... **All Distilled Alcohol Is Gluten/Casein/Soy Free* [2]

Wine... **All Wine Made In The USA Is Gluten/Casein/Soy Free* [2]

Wing Sauce

   Frank's RedHot - Chile 'N Lime, Original, Xtra Hot

   Moore's Marinade - Honey BBQ Wing, Original, Teriyaki

Wings... **All Fresh Chicken Is Gluten/Casein/Soy Free (Non-Marinated, Unseasoned)*

   Wegmans - Chicken Wings

Worcestershire Sauce

   Great Value Brand (Wal-Mart)

   Hannaford Brand

   Lea & Perrins - Original

   Safeway Brand

X

Xanthan Gum

   Authentic Foods ▲

   Bob's Red Mill ▲

   El Peto ▲

   Ener-G ▲

   Gluten-Free Essentials ▲

   Kinnikinnick ▲

Y Y

Z

Yams... **All **Fresh** Yams Are **Gluten/Casein/Soy Free***

   S&W - Candied Yams

   Spartan Brand - Yams

Yeast

   Bob's Red Mill▲ - Yeast (Active Dry, Nutritional T6635)

   El Peto▲

   Fleischmann's - All Varieties

   Hodgson Mill▲ - Active Dry, Fast Rise

   Red Star - Active Dry, Bread Machine, Cake, Quick Rise

Yellow Squash... see Squash

Yogurt

   Nogurt - Organic (Banana Cinnamon, Blueberry, Chocolate, Orange, Pomegranate)

   Ricera - Organic (Blueberry, Peach, Strawberry, Vanilla)

   So Delicious - Coconut Milk (Blueberry, Chocolate, Passionate Mango, Plain, Pina Colada, Raspberry, Strawberry, Strawberry Banana, Vanilla)

Z

Zucchini... **All **Fresh** Zucchini Is **Gluten/Casein/Soy Free***

Gluten/Casein/Soy Free
Over The Counter (OTC) Pharmacy Guide

Rx

Rx   ## After Shave/Shaving Gel

Arbonne - NutriMinC RE9 Resurface Shave Gel
Burt's Bees - Men's Natural Shave Cream

Allergy/Sinus/Cold/Flu Relief

Afrin - Nasal Spray (All Varieties)
Airborne -
  Lemon Lime
  On The Go Lemon Lime
  Original
  Pink Grapefruit
  Very Berry
California Baby - Colds & Flu Massage Oil
Claritin - D24, Ready Tabs
Cold-Eeze - Cold Remedy Lozenges (All Flavors)
Dayquil -
  Cold & Flu Liquid
  Cough Liquid
  Mucus Control Expectorant Liquid
  Mucus Control DM Expectorant Cough Suppressant Liquid
Halls - Cherry, Ice Blue, Mentho Lyptus, Strawberry, Tropical Fruit
Meijer -
  Apap
    Cough Cold (Infant Drops Cherry)
    PE Allergy Sinus Caplets
    PE Cold Flu Day Cool Caplets
    PE Cold Severe Congestion Caplets

allergy/sinus/cold/flu relief

Diphedryl (Tablets)   **Rx**
Loratadine (D 24hr Tablets)
Nasal Spray (Liquid, Multi Symptom Liquid, No Drip Pump Liquid)
Nitetime 6 hr (Cherry Liquid, Liquid Gels, Original Liquid)
Nitetime Cough 6 hr (Cherry Liquid)
Triacting Nitetime Grape Liquid
Tussin (Cough Cold Softgels)

Nyquil -
Cold & Flu Liquid (Cherry, Original)
Cough Liquid (Cherry)
D Cold & Flu Liquid (Original)
Less Drowsy Cold & Flu Liquid (Original)

Safeway Select -
Allergy Relief
Mucous Relief (DM & PE)

Theraflu -
Thin Strips (Daytime Cold & Cough, Nightime Cold & Cough)
Warming Relief Syrups (Daytime)

Vicks -
Formula 44 Custom Care Sore Throat Spray
   Berry Burst
   Honey Lemon Burst
Formula 44 Liquid
   Body Aches
   Chesty Cough
   Congestion
   Cough & Cold PM
   Dry Cough

Rx   Antacids

Lactaid - Dietary Supplement (Fast Act Caplets, Fast Act Chewables)
Meijer -
     Antacid Calcium (Peppermint Chewables, XS Berry Chewables, XS Chewables, XS Tropical Chewables, XS Wintergreen Chewables)
     Cimetidine Tablets
     Effervescent Antacid Pain Tablets
     Milk Of Magnesia (Mint Liquid, Original Liquid)
     Pink Bismuth (Chewables, Maximum Strength Liquid, Regular Strength Liquid)
     Ranitidine
Pepto Bismol - All Varieties
Safeway Select - Antacid Tablets (Fruit Flavored, Peppermint, Wintergreen)
Tagamet - HB

Antibiotic/Analgesic Ointment & Spray

Cortaid - All Varieties
Hy-Vee -
     First Aid (Allergy Creme 2%, Antibiotic Ointment, Hydrocortisone Cream 1%)
     Isopropyl Alcohol

Anti-Diarrhea

Lactaid - Dietary Supplement (Fast Act Caplets, Fast Act Chewables)
Meijer - Pink Bismuth (Chewables, Maximum Strength Liquid, Regular Strength Liquid)
Pepto Bismol - All Varieties

Anti-Gas

Rx

Lactaid - Dietary Supplement (Fast Act Caplets, Fast Act Chewables)

Cosmetics

Afterglow Cosmetics▲ - All Products
Arbonne -
   About Face
      Blusher
      Brow Wax
      Cream Concealer
      Eye Pencil
      Eye Shadow
      Line Defiance Liquid Foundation SPF 15
      Lip Pencil
      Mineral Powder Foundation SPF 15
      Sheer Shine
      Translucent Powder (Loose, Pressed)
      Wipe Out Eye Makeup Remover
   Before Sun No Sun Intended Bronzing Powder

Cough Drops/Sore Throat Spray/Lozenges

Cold-Eeze - Cold Remedy Lozenges (All Flavors)
Halls - Cherry, Ice Blue, Mentho Lyptus, Strawberry, Tropical Fruit
Hy-Vee - Cherry Eucalyptus Flavor Drops, Honey Lemon Cough Drops,
   Sugar Free Black Cherry Drops

Rx **Organix** - Organic Cough & Sore Throat Drops (Golden Honey Lemon, Orchard Cherry)

Safeway Select - Cough Drops (Cherry, Honey Lemon)

Vicks - Formula 44 Custom Care Sore Throat Spray (Berry Burst, Honey Lemon Burst)

Walgreens - Cough Drops (Sugar Free Menthol)

Hair Care

Burt's Bees -
  Color Keeper (Conditioner)
  Super Shiny Grapefruit Sugarbeet (Conditioner)
California Baby -
  Calendula Hair Conditioner
  Calendula Shampoo & Bodywash
  Calming Hair Conditioner
  Calming Hair Detangler
  Calming Shampoo & Body Wash
  Super Sensitive Hair Conditioner
  Super Sensitive Shampoo & Bodywash
  Swimmer's Defense Shampoo & Body Wash
  Tea Tree & Lavender Shampoo & Body Wash
Desert Essence Organics -
  Conditioner (Fragrance Free, Green Apple & Ginger, Italian Red Grape, Red Raspberry)
  Shampoo (Fragrance Free, Green Apple & Ginger, Italian Red Grape, Lemon Tea Tree, Red Raspberry)
Gluten-Free Savonnerie▲ - All Products
Hy-Vee -
  Baby Shampoo
  Extra Body Shampoo Plus Conditioner

Le Techniq (Truly Clean Pro Vitamin Shampoo)
Lice Killing Shampoo
Lice Shampoo & Cream Rinse
Lice Treatment Kit
Normal Vitamin Shampoo & Conditioner

Rx

Johnson's - Baby Shampoo
Keys - All Products
Meijer - Minoxidil 5% Liquid (30 Day, 90 Day)
Pantene Pro-V -
Always Smooth (Conditioner, Shampoo)
Anti Frizz (Conditioner, Shampoo)
Beautiful Lengths (Conditioner, Shampoo)
Classic Care (Conditioner, Shampoo)
Color Revival (Conditioner, Shampoo)
Daily Moisture Renewal (Conditioner, Shampoo)
Full & Thick (Conditioner, Shampoo)
Sheer Volume (Conditioner, Shampoo)

Laxatives/Hemorrhoidal Relief

Citrucel - Fiber Therapy Powder (Orange Regular, Orange Sugar Free)
Fleet - Fiber Gummies
Konsyl - Original Natural Fiber Supplement
Meijer -
Fiber Therapy Caplets
Hemorrhoidal (Suppository)
Laxative Tablets (Natural MS, Senna)
NVP (Capsules, Original Orange Powder, Original Regular Powder, Smooth Orange Powder, Sugar Free Smooth Orange Powder)

Rx **Metamucil** -
> Capsules (Plus Calcium, Regular)
> Powder Coarse Milled Original Texture (Orange, Unflavored)
> Powder Smooth Texture (Orange)

Pedia-Lax -
> Chewable Tablets (Watermelon)
> Liquid Stool Softener (Fruit Punch)
> Quick Dissolve Strips

Tucks - Hemorroidal Ointment, Hydrocortisone Anti Itch Ointment, Medicated Pads, Take Along Medicated Pads

Lip Care

Arbonne -
> Before Sun Lip Saver SPF 30
> Bio Nutria Herbal Lip Ointment
> Bio Nutria Lip Service Dietary Supplement
> F.Y.I. It Shines Lip Gloss

Blistex -
> Clear Advance
> Deep Renewal
> Gentle Sense
> Herbal Answer Gel
> Lip Balm (Berry, Medicated, Mint)
> Lip Medex
> Lip Ointment
> Lip Revitalizer
> Raspberry Lemonade Blast
> Silk & Shine
> Ultra Protection

Burt's Bees -   **Rx**

    Lip Balm (Honey, Medicated)

    Lipshimmer (All Shades)

Desert Essence Organics -

    Lip Tints

        Coconut

        Italian Red Grape

        Red Raspberry

        Vanilla Chai

Miscellaneous Products

Band-Aid - Flexible Fabric

Burt's Bees -

    Bug Bite Relief

    Herbal Blemish Stick

    Herbal Deodorant

    Therapeutic Bath Crystals

Meijer -

    Miconazole Cream (3 Day Preapp. Combo, 3 Day Disapp. Combo, 7 Day Disapp., 7 Day Reapp.)

    Nicotine Gum (Mint, Regular)

    Tioconazole 1 Day Ointment (Disapp.)

Nature's Baby Organics - All Purpose Deodorizer

Nicorette -

    Chewing Gum

        Fresh Mint (2 mg, 4 mg)

        Fruit Chill (2 mg, 4 mg)

        White Ice Mint (2 mg, 4 mg)

Rx   Oral Hygiene

Aquafresh -
- Toothpaste
  - Cavity Protection
  - Extra Fresh
  - Sensitive

Colgate -
- Toothpaste
  - Cavity Protection (Regular)
  - Luminous (Crystal Clean Mint)

Crest - All Mouthrinses, All Toothpaste Varieties, All Whitestrips

Glide - Floss

Kirkman Labs - Toothpaste Gel

Listerine -
- Agent Cool Blue Tinting Rinse
- Antiseptic Mouthwash (All Varieties) *(Except Citrus)*
- Pocket Paks Oral Care Strips (Cinnamon, Cool Mint, Fresh Burst)
- Tooth Defense Anticavity Fluoride Rinse
- Totalcare Anticavity Mouthwash
- Whitening Pre Brush Rinse
- Whitening Quick Dissolving Strips
- Whitening Vibrant White Rinse

Polident - Denture Cleanser

Scope - Mouthwash (Original, Peppermint)

Sensodyne - Pronamel Toothpaste

Tom's Of Maine -
- Floss Antiplaque Flat
- Floss Antiplaque Round

ZOOM - Whitening Gel *(At The Dentist)*

Pain Relief   **Rx**

Meijer -
  Apap (Caplet, Cool Caplet, ER Caplet Red, ER Caplet White, ETS Tablet, Gelcap, Geltab, Tablet)
  Aspirin
    Adult Orange Chewables
    Child Orange Chewables
  Headache Tablets
  Ibuprofen
    Caplets Brown
    Caplets Orange
    Junior Caplet
    Tablets Brown
    Tablets Orange
  Migraine Caplets
  Naproxen Sodium (Caplets, Tablets)
Safeway Select -
  Ibuprofen (Liquid Softgels)
  Non Aspirin Extra Strength (Capsules)
  Pain Reliever Fever Reducer Tablets

Play Dough

Aroma Dough - All Natural Playing Dough
Bloom Putty - Play Putty (Scented, Unscented)
Bluedominoes - Organic Activity Dough●
Max's Mud - Organic Sculpting Dough

Rx   Skin Care

Arbonne -
  Aromassentials
    Awaken Sea Salt Scrub 16 oz.
    Unwind (Bath Salts, Massage Oil)
  Bio Nutria
    Herbal (Muscle Massage Gel, Vapor Rub)
    Leg Vein Formula
  Clear Advantage
    Acne Lotion
    Refining Toner
    Skin Support Supplement
    Spot Treatment
  FC5
    Moisturizing Night Crème
    Nurturing Day Lotion w/SPF 20
    Oil Absorbing Day Lotion w/SPF 20
    Purifying Cleanser + Toner
    Skin Conditioning Oil
    Ultra Hydrating Hand Crème
  F.Y.I.
    Body Better Body Cream
    Eye Q Cream Eye Shadow
    Get Even Tinted Moisturizer SPF 15
    Sugar Slush Body Scrub
  Figure 8
    Vanish (Pre Shower Cellulite Scrub, Water Relief Treatment Serum)
  NutriMinC RE9
    Regain Illuminating Enzyme Peel
    Retaliate Wrinkle Filler

skin care

Revelâge **Rx**

    Age Spot Brightening Day Cream w/SPF 30

    Age Spot Brightening Hand Therapy w/SPF 30

    Concentrated Age Spot Minimizer

    Intensive Pro Brightening Night Serum

SeaSource Detox Spa

    5 In I Essential Massage Oil

    Foaming Sea Salt Scrub

    Purifying Sea Soak

    Remineralizing Body Lotion 24 Hr.

    Renewing Body Gelée

    Sea Mud Face and Body Mask

Burt's Bees -

    After Sun Soother

    Almond Milk Hand Crème

    Baby Bee (Diaper Ointment, Dusting Powder)

    Beeswax Moist (Day Creme, Night Crème)

    Deep Pore Scrub

    Garden Tomato Toner

    Hand Sanitizer

    Healthy Treatment (Evening Primrose Overnight Crème, Pore Refining Mask, Royal Jelly Eye Crème, Shea Butter Hand Repair)

    Soothingly Sensitive Lotion

    Thoroughly Therapeutic (Body Butter, Foot Cream, Hand Cream, Lotion)

California Baby -

    Aloe Vera Cream

    Botanical Moisturizing Cream

    Calendula (Cream, Everyday Lotion)

    Calming (Diaper Rash Cream, Everyday Lotion, Massage Oil, Non Talc Powder, Soothing & Healing Spray)

Rx   Citronella (SPF 30+ Sunscreen Lotion, Summer Lotion)

      Colds & Flu Massage Oil

      Everyday/Year Round SPF 30 (Sunblock Stick, Sunscreen Lotion)

      I Love You Aromatherapy Massage Oil

      Overtired & Cranky Massage Oil

      Sunblock Stick SPF 30 (No Fragrance)

      Sunscreen SPF 30 (Citronella, No Fragrance)

      Sunscreen Lotion SPF 18 (No Fragrance)

      Super Sensitive (Everyday Lotion, Massage Oil)

Clear & Clear - Foaming Facial Cleaner (Oil Free, Sensitive Skin)

Coppertone -

      Oil Free Lotion (SPF 15, SPF 30)

      Sport Lotion (SPF 15, SPF 30, SPF 50, SPF 50 Faces)

      Suncreen Tanning Lotion (SPF 4, SPF 8)

      Waterbabies Sunblock Stick (SPF 30)

      Waterbabies Sunscreen Lotion (SPF 50, SPF 50 Pure & Simple)

Desert Essence Organics -

      Age Reversal Pomegranate (Eye Serum, Face Serum)

      Age Reversal SPF 30 Mineral Sunscreen

      Almond Hand & Body Lotion

      Bulgarian Lavender Hand & Body Lotion

      Coconut Hand & Body Lotion

      Pistachio Foot Repair Cream

      Pumpkin Hand Repair Cream

      Spicy Citrus Hand & Body Lotion

      Vanilla Chai Hand & Body Lotion

Eucerin - Original Lotion

Gluten-Free Savonnerie▲ - All Products

Rx

Hy-Vee -
   Skin Cream (Total Moisture)
   Therapeutic Skin Lotion
Johnson's - Baby Oil
Keys - All Products
Lubriderm -
   Daily Moisture Lotion
      Fragrance Free
      Regular
      Sensitive Skin
      w/Sea Kelp Extract
      w/Shea & Cocoa Butters
Nature's Baby Organics -
   Ah Choo Chest Rub
   Baby Oil
   Diaper Ointment
   Face & Body Moisturizer
   Silky Dusting Powder
   Soothing Stick

Sleep Aids

Meijer -
   Apap PM
      Caplets
      Gelcaps
      Geltabs
   Sleep Aid Nitetime (Caplets)

Rx   Soap

Arbonne -
    Aromassentials
        Awaken Sea Salt Scrub 16 oz.
        Unwind Bath Salts
    Bio Nutria Herbal Vapor Soak
    Clear Advantage
        Acne Wash
        Refining Toner
    FC5
        Exfoliating New Cell Scrub
        Purifying Cleanser + Toner
    F.Y.I. Sugar Slush Body Scrub
    Figure 8 Vanish Pre Shower Cellulite Scrub
    SeaSource Detox Spa
        Foaming Sea Salt Scrub
        Purifying Sea Soak
Burts Bees - Men's Natural Bar Soap
California Baby -
    Bubble Bath (Calendula, Calming, Chamomile & Herbs, Colds & Flu, I Love You, Light & Happy, Overtired & Cranky, Party, Super Sensitive)
    Calendula Shampoo & Body Wash
    Calming Shampoo & Body Wash
    Diaper Area Wash
    Handwash (First Aid Moisturizing, Natural Antibacterial Blend Moisturizing, Super Sensitive)
    Natural Pregnancy Body Wash
    Swimmer's Defense Shampoo & Body Wash
    Tea Tree & Lavender Shampoo & Body Wash

supplements

Rx

Dial - Liquid Hand Soap
Fleurish Beauty - Aloe & Shea Body Wash
Gluten-Free Savonnerie▲ - All Products
Goodnight Moon Soaps - All Soaps & Sprays
Johnson's - Head To Toe Baby Wash
Keys - All Products
Tom's Of Maine - Body Bar (Natural Deodorant)

Stay Awake

Meijer - Stay Awake Tablets
Ultra Pep-Back

Supplements

Aqua Flow - Enzymatic Therapy
Arbonne - Smart Nutritional Hybrids Daily Nutritional Chews For Teens, Smart Nutritional Hybrids Daily Power Punch For Kids
Carlson -
   Alpha Lipoic Acid Tablets
   Bioflavonoids
   Blood Nutrients
   Buffalo Liver
   Cardi Rite
   Carlson For Kids Chewable DHA
   Carlson For Kids Cod Liver Oil
   Carlson For Kids Very Finest Fish Oil (Lemon, Orange)
   Chelated Chromium

Rx Cod Liver Oil (Lemon, Regular, w/Low Vitamin A)
Creatine
DLPA
Digestive Aid
E Gem Lip Care
E Gem Oil Drops
E Gem Shampoo
Empty Gelatin
EPA Gems
Fish Oil Q
Folic Acid
GLA
Garlic
Glucosamine Sulfate Capsules
Glutathione Booster
Glycine
Golden Primrose
HCL & Pepsin
Healthy Mood 5 HTP Elite
Heartbeat Elite Scientifically Complete
Hi Fiber
Homocysteine Guard
Kelp
Key E Cream
Key E Kaps
Key E Ointment
Key E Powder
L Alanine
L Arginine Capsules
L Arginine Powder
L Asparagine

supplements

Rx

L Aspartic Acid
L Carnitine
L Glutamic Acid
L Glutamine (Capsules, Powder)
L Lysine (Capsules, Powder)
L Methionine (Capsules, Powder)
L Proline (Capsules, Powder)
L Serine
L Threonine
Lightly Lemon
Lutein 6 MG
Lycopene (Tomato Free)
MSM Sulfur
Medomega Fish Oil
Mellow Mood
Moly B
Mother's DHA
NAC (Capsules, Powder)
Nutra Support Joint Cartilage Builder
P5P
Pantethine Time
Pantothenic Acid Time
Pro Rite
Psyllium
Ribose
Right For The Liver
Right For The Macula
Rutin Quercetin
Salmon Oil
Salmon Oil & GLA
Super Cod Liver Oil

Rx Super Daily Amino Blend (Capsules, Powder)
Super DHA Gems
Super Omega 3 Gems
Taurine
Tocotrienols
Tri B Homocysteine Formula
Very Finest Fish Oil Lemon Flavor (Liquid)
Very Finest Fish Oil Orange Flavor (Liquid)

Country Life -
Activated Charcoal Caplets●
Bee Propolis Veg Caplets●
Bio Active Hyaluronic Acid●
Brewer's Yeast Tablets●
Celadrin●
Clatonalin●
Cod Liver Oil●
CoQ10●
Daily Dophilus●
Daily Fiber X Veg Caplets●
Easy Iron●
Enhanced QM 1●
Estro G Balance●
Evening Primrose Oil●
Genaslim●
Green Edge II Powder●
Lipotropic Metabolizer●
Maxi Sorb CoQ10●
Natural Acidophilus w/Pectin Veg Caplets●
Norwegian Kelp●
Omega 3●

Power Dophilus Veg Caplets●   **Rx**
RNA/DNA●
Resveratrol Plus●
Shark Cartilage Veg Caplets●
Shark Liver Oil●
Stress Shield●
Super Fiber Psyllium Seed Husk Powder●
Ultra Oils●
Ultra Omegas DHA/EPA●
Zinc Picolinate●

Kirkman Labs -

Acetyl L Carnitine
Acidophilus Powder
Alpha Ketoglutaric Acid
Alpha Lipoic Acid
Amino Support (Capsules, Powder)
Bifido Complex (Regular)
BioCore Dairy
Buffered Magnesium (Glycinate Bio Max Series Powder, Oxide)
Carb Digest w/Isogest
Chromium
Cod Liver Oil (Lemon Lime Liquid, Regular Liquid, w/Vitamins A & D)
Coenzyme Q10 (Capsules, Chewable Tablets, Tablets)
Colostrum Gold (Flavored, Unflavored)
Creatine (Capsules)
DMAE (Capsules, Chewable Wafers)
DMG (Capsules, Capsules w/Folic Acid & B12, Capsules w/Folinic Acid & B12, Liquid, Maximum Strength, w/B12 & Folinic Acid Liquid)
DPP IV Forte

Rx DRN (Detoxification Booster Capsules, Lithium, Vitamin/Mineral Basic Supplement Powder, Vitamin/Mineral LDA Basic Supplement)

Detox Aid Advanced Formula

Detoxification Aid Pro Support II

EFA Powder

EnZym Aid Multi Enzyme Complex

EnZym Complete DPP IV II (Regular, w/Isogest)

Everyday Multi Vitamin (Regular, w/o Vitamins A & D)

Folic Acid (Chewable Tablets, w/B12 Capsules, w/B12 Liquid)

Folinic Acid (Capsules, w/B12 Liquid)

GABA (Plain, w/Niacinamide & Inositol)

Gastro Support

Gastromune AI Support

Ginkgo Biloba

Glucosamine Sulfate

Glycine

Grape Extract

Grapefruit Seed Extract

Idebenone

Immuno Aid

Inositol Pure Soluble Powder

Iron Bio Max Series (Capsules, Liquid)

L Glutamine

L Taurine

Lactobacillus Acidophilus

Lactobacillus Duo

Magnesium Citrate Soluble Powder

Magnesium Glycinate Bio Max Series

Magnesium Malate

Magnesium Sulfate Cream

Maximum Spectrum Enzyme Complete/DPP IV Fruit Free **Rx**
  w/Isogest

Melatonin (Chewables, Plus Magnesium, Slo Release Tablets)

Methylcobalamin Concentrated Powder

Milk Thistle

Mito Cell Support

Molybdenum

Multi Enzyme Formula

Multi Flora Spectrum

N Acetyl Cysteine

Nu Thera (Everyday, Everyday Companion, w/P5P, w/o Vitamins A & D)

P5P (Regular, w/Magnesium Glycinate)

Peptidase Complete

Phenol Assist (Companion, Regular)

Pro Bio (Chewable Wafers, Defense, Gold, Inulin Free)

Pro Culture Gold

Pro Immune Support

Reduced L Glatathione (Capsules, Lotion)

Saccharomyces Boulardii

Selenium

Spectrum Complete (Capsules, Powder Flavored, Powder Regular)

Super Cranberry Extract (Capsules, Chewables)

Super NuThera (Caplets, Capsules, Challenge Powders, Lemon Lime
  Liquid, New Improved Powder, Powder, Raspberry Flavored
  Concentrate, Tropical Fruit Liquid, w/P5P Caplets, w/P5P Lemon Lime
  Flavored Concentrate, w/P5P Liquid, w/P5P New Improved Powder,
  w/P5P Powder, w/o Vitamins A & D (Cherry Liquid, Regular, Tropical
  Fruit Liquid))

Super Pro Bio (Bio Max Series)

TMG (Capsules, Capsules w/Folic Acid & B12, Liquid w/Folinic Acid &
  B12, Powder w/Folic Acid & B12, w/Folic Acid & B12, w/Folinic Acid &
  B12, w/Folinic Acid & Methyl B12)

Rx   Thera Response

Threelac

Vanadium

Yeast Aid (Capsules, Powder)

Meijer -

Echinacea

Gingko Biloba

Glucosamine & Collagen & HA

Glucosamine Chondroitin (3X, Extra Strength, Plus MSM)

Glucosamine Sulfate Caplets

Green Tea

Panax Ginseng

Vision Formula w/Lutein

Member's Mark (Sam's Club) -

Gingko Biloba

Glucosamine Chondroitin Triple Strength

Nature's Bounty - Glucosamine Chondroitin Complex Xtra Strength

Osteo Bi-Flex - (Double Strength Tablets, Strength Tablets)

Vitamins & Minerals

Carlson -

B 12 SL

B 12 Time

B Compleet

Baby Drops Vitamin D

Biotin

Carlson For Kids Chewable Calcium

Carlson For Kids Chewable Vitamin C

Chelated Cal Mag

vitamins & minerals

Chelated Calcium **Rx**
Chelated Copper
Chelated Iron
Chelated Magnanese
Chelated Magnesium
Chelated Mineral Compleet
Chelated Zinc
Chew Iron
Chewable Calcium Citrate
Complexed Potassium
D Alpha Gems
D Drops (1000 IU, 2000 IU)
E Gems
E Gems Elite
E Gems Plus
Gamma E Gems
Magnesium
Mild C (Capsules, Chewable, Crystals, Timed Release)
Mini Multi
Niacin
Niacin Amide
Niacin Time
One Gram C
Potassium
Selenium (Capsules, Tablets)
Solar D Gems
Super C Complex
Super D Omega 3
Time C
Time C Bio
Veg E Gems

Rx   Vitamin A Pamitate
Vitamin A Solubilized
Vitamin Bl
Vitamin B2
Vitamin B6 (Liquid, Tablets)
Vitamin C Crystals
Vitamin D
Zinc
Zinc Ease

Country Life -
Action B Caplets●
Basic B Caplets●
Bio Rutin Complex●
Biotin●
Buffered Vitamin C●
Cap C Veg Caplets●
Chewable Acerola C Complex●
Chewable Orange Juice●
Chewable Vitamin E●
Choline●
Choline Inositol Complex●
Citrus Bioflavonoids●
Coenzyme Active B6●
Dry Vitamin D 1000 IU●
Ester C●
Ester C Veg Caplets●
Flush Free Niacin Veg Caplets●
Folic Acid●
Grape Complete Caps●

Rx

Grape Seed Extract Veg Caps●
Hi Potency Biotin●
Hi Potency Biotin Veg Caps●
Hi Potency Maxi B Caps●
Inositol Powder●
Lutein●
Maxi C Complex Vitamin C●
Niacin●
Niacinamide●
Paba●
Pantothenic Acid●
Rutin●
Special C Complex●
Stress M●
Sublingual Vitamin B12●
Super Potency Action B●
Super Potency Hi B●
Superior Vitamin C●
Supreme Hi B●
Tall Tree Children's Chewable Vitamin C●
Vitamin B1●
Vitamin B2●
Vitamin B6●
Vitamin B6 Veg Caplets●
Vitamin B12●
Vitamin C●
Vitamin C Crystals●
Vitamin D3●
Vitamin K1●

Rx Kirkman Labs -

Advanced Adult Multi Vitamin

Advanced Mineral Support

B Complex w/CoEnzymes Pro Support (Capsules, Powder)

Buffered Vitamin C Powder

Calcium Bio Max Series

Calcium Magnesium Liquid

Calcium w/Vitamin D (Chewable Tablets, Powder Unflavored)

Calcium w/o Vitamin D Bio Max Series

Children's Chewable Multi Vitamin/Mineral (Capsules, Wafers)

D Biotin

Multi Mineral Complex Pro Support

Multi Vitamin Pro Support

Mycellized Vitamin A Liquid

Perry Prenatal

Vitamin B6 (Magnesium Vitamin/Mineral Chewable Wafers, Regular)

Vitamin C (Bio Max Series Buffered Powder Flavored, Bio Max Series
  Buffered Powder Unflavored, Capsules, Chewables, Tablets)

Vitamin D

Vitamin D3

Vitamin E

Zinc (Bio Max Series, Liquid, Sulfate, w/Vitamin C & Slippery Elm
      Lozenges)

Meijer -

Calcium (Coral, Plus D)

Ester C

Slow Release Iron

Vitamin B Complex w/Vitamin C

Vitamin B6 Natural

Vitamin B12 Tablets

Vitamin C Natural

Vitamin E Synthetic Softgels

Member's Mark (Sam's Club) -

Rx

Chewable Multi Complete
Children's Multivitamin Gummies
Complete Multi
Iron Slow Release
Niacin
Super B Complex w/Vitamin C
Vitamin B Complex w/Vitamin C
Vitamin B12
Vitamin C w/Natural Rose Hips
Ocuvite - Lutein (Capsules, Tablets)
Safeway Select - Vitamin C
Schiff - Niacin Flush Free (Tablets)
Slice Of Life - Gummy Vitamins For Adults (All Varieties)
Yummi Bears - All Varieties (Organic, Regular)

Weight Loss

Arbonne - Figure 8 On the Go! Weight Loss Chews (Creamy Caramel, Peanut Butter)
CitriMax Plus

Index

index

index

index

NOTES

NOTES

NOTES

NOTES

NOTES

Making Gluten-Free Living Easy!

Cecelia's Marketplace

Kalamazoo, Michigan

www.CeceliasMarketplace.com

Quick Order Form

Online Orders: www.CeceliasMarketplace.com

✉ Mail Orders: Kal-Haven Publishing
P.O. Box 20383
Kalamazoo, MI 49019
U.S.A.

Cecelia's Marketplace	Quantity	Price	Total

Gluten-Free
Grocery Shopping Guide _____ (x $24.95) = _____

Gluten/Casein Free
Grocery Shopping Guide _____ (x $24.95) = _____

Gluten/Casein/Soy Free
Grocery Shopping Guide _____ (x $24.95) = _____

Sales Tax: Michigan residents please add 6% sales tax _____

Sub Total: _____

Shipping: (quantities 1-2 add $5.25)
(quantities 3-6 add $9.95) _____

Total: _____

*Please make check or money order payable to Kal-Haven Publishing

Name: _____

Address:_____

City:_____State:_____Zip:_____

Email address:_____

Making Gluten-Free Living Easy!

Cecelia's Marketplace

Kalamazoo, Michigan

www.CeceliasMarketplace.com

Quick Order Form

Online Orders: www.CeceliasMarketplace.com

Mail Orders: Kal-Haven Publishing
P.O. Box 20383
Kalamazoo, MI 49019
U.S.A.

Cecelia's Marketplace	Quantity	Price	Total
Gluten-Free Grocery Shopping Guide	_____	(x $24.95) =	_____
Gluten/Casein Free Grocery Shopping Guide	_____	(x $24.95) =	_____
Gluten/Casein/Soy Free Grocery Shopping Guide	_____	(x $24.95) =	_____

Sales Tax: Michigan residents please add 6% sales tax   _____

Sub Total: _____

Shipping: (quantities 1-2 add $5.25)
(quantities 3-6 add $9.95)   _____

Total: _____

*Please make check or money order payable to Kal-Haven Publishing

Name: _____

Address: _____

City: _____ State: _____ Zip: _____

Email address: _____

Making Gluten-Free Living Easy!

Cecelia's Marketplace
Kalamazoo, Michigan

www.CeceliasMarketplace.com

Quick Order Form

Online Orders: www.CeceliasMarketplace.com

Mail Orders: Kal-Haven Publishing
P.O. Box 20383
Kalamazoo, MI 49019
U.S.A.

Cecelia's Marketplace	Quantity	Price	Total
Gluten-Free Grocery Shopping Guide	_____	(x $24.95) =	_____
Gluten/Casein Free Grocery Shopping Guide	_____	(x $24.95) =	_____
Gluten/Casein/Soy Free Grocery Shopping Guide	_____	(x $24.95) =	_____

Sales Tax: Michigan residents please add 6% sales tax _____

Sub Total: _____

Shipping: (quantities 1-2 add $5.25)
(quantities 3-6 add $9.95) _____

Total: _____

*Please make check or money order payable to Kal-Haven Publishing

Name: _____

Address: _____

City: _____ State: _____ Zip: _____

Email address: _____

Making Gluten-Free Living Easy!

Cecelia's Marketplace

Kalamazoo, Michigan

www.CeceliasMarketplace.com

Quick Order Form

🖳 **Online Orders:** www.CeceliasMarketplace.com

✉ **Mail Orders:** Kal-Haven Publishing
P.O. Box 20383
Kalamazoo, MI 49019
U.S.A.

Cecelia's Marketplace	Quantity	Price	Total
Gluten-Free Grocery Shopping Guide	_____	(x $24.95) =	_____
Gluten/Casein Free Grocery Shopping Guide	_____	(x $24.95) =	_____
Gluten/Casein/Soy Free Grocery Shopping Guide	_____	(x $24.95) =	_____

Sales Tax: Michigan residents please add 6% sales tax _____

Sub Total: _____

Shipping: (quantities 1-2 add $5.25)
(quantities 3-6 add $9.95) _____

Total: _____

*Please make check or money order payable to Kal-Haven Publishing

Name: _____

Address: _____

City: _____ State: _____ Zip: _____

Email address: _____